REIKI HISTORY

REAL REIKI®
FROM JAPAN
TO THE WESTERN WORLD

Shoshana Shay

Radiance Associates
St. Petersburg, Florida

ISBN-13 978-0-933267-20-6
First edition

Published by Radiance Associates
P.O. Box 67352, St. Pete Beach FL 33736

Library of Congress Cataloging-in-Publication Data

Names: Shay, Shoshana, author.
Title: Reiki history : Real Reiki® from Japan to the western world / Shoshana Shay.
Description: St. Petersburg, Florida : Radiance Associates, [2019] | Includes bibliographical references.
Identifiers: ISBN 9780933267206 | ISBN 9780933267268 (ebook)
Subjects: LCSH: Reiki (Healing system)--History. | Takata, Hawayo Kawamuri, 1900-1980. | Ray, Barbara (Barbara Weber), 1941- | Women healers--Biography. | LCGFT: Biographies.
Classification: LCC RZ403.R45 S53 2019 (print) | LCC RZ403.R45 (ebook) | DDC 615.852--dc23

Printed in the United States of America.

TABLE OF CONTENTS

LIST OF ILLUSTRATIONS

A NOTE ABOUT TERMINOLOGY AND WORDING

The word "reiki" in the twenty-first century is a generic term. It can be used by anyone to mean anything. Generally "reiki" refers to some kind of healing practice... but what that consists of and how it is taught and applied varies widely. Before approximately 1976, the word "Reiki" referred exclusively to a kind of energy healing offered by a Japanese-American woman named Hawayo Takata.

In this book, the word "Reiki" is used without quotes for any of the history before 1981 and for any references to what Mrs. Takata herself did. "Reiki" or "reiki things" (in quotes) refer to things which other people started to advertise and do which were not intact and not what Mrs. Takata knew. Real Reiki® and Authentic Reiki® are used to refer to the intact science as taught by Mrs. Takata, and to differentiate that intact system from other things when examining Mrs. Takata's legacy.

The name of the state of Hawai'i is spelled both with and without a glottal stop ('). Officially, because the statehood act of 1959 did not use the glottal stop, the state is spelled "Hawaii." It would take an Act of Congress to change this. However, the official place name for the island in that state is "Hawai'i".[1] In general, in this book Hawaiian place names are spelled the way they would have been at the time, especially when quoting from historical documents.

FOREWORD

When I first considered researching the history of "reiki," I had barely been using the term "reiki" in my own professional outreach as an Authorized Instructor of Real Reiki®, The Radiance Technique®. There is so much confusion, since "reiki" is a generic term, that I really prefer to present information about The Radiance Technique®, Authentic Reiki® free from preconceptions based on vague ideas about some "reiki thing." However, I especially wanted to understand how a little Japanese-Hawaiian woman managed to learn and protect a sacred science most of the way through the twentieth century.

I am an historian by inclination and education. My history professors at Bryn Mawr College would probably not be surprised at this topic, since I loved to research things like the development of plate glass and how it affected shopping trends in nineteenth-century England (not your traditional topic for historical research).

Making my way through the primary, contemporary sources about Hawayo Takata, Dr. Barbara Ray, Reiki and Real Reiki® has been very educational. There are a fair number of negative, nasty articles and letters out there about one and another person involved with Reiki in the chaotic transition around Mrs. Takata's death. For the most part, in this book I do not name names except when they are historically relevant. The endnotes and bibliography cite key quoted sources for this study; the large majority of the negativity is irrelevant in relation to actual historical facts.

Most of all, my Gratitude to and for Dr. Barbara Ray has expanded immensely. If she had not recognized in her first contact with Reiki that there was more than she was told; if she had not persisted in finding who knew that "more;" and if she had not taken on the monumental task of making Reiki available in a Western context, the intact, unaltered science of Real Reiki® would not be available for us today. Dr. Ray stood steady through others' attacks, slanders, hatred, wounded pride, jealousy and ignorance. Her clarity and vision have never wavered and her responses to these other people were (in my personal opinion) remarkably generous and patient. She could have chosen to continue her successful career as a college professor. Instead, Dr. Ray devoted her life to the intact science of Reiki, also known as The Radiance Technique®. Every single person who has benefited from the real Authentic Reiki® owes Dr. Ray their thanks.

Shoshana Shay
September 2019

INTRODUCTION

The history of Reiki in the West is filled with stories, most of which were made up by people who did not have firsthand information. This book is a history-based look at what really happened: how Reiki was brought to the United States from Japan and how it spread around the world.

The best research for this kind of history uses original documents of the time and original material which is as contemporaneous as possible. When it was possible to interview people who were actually there, interviews have helped to fill out the story. However, there is ample data from the times themselves, especially given we have actual written material serving as a record of specific events. This book traces the roots of Reiki based on the facts available.

Reiki was brought from Japan to the West by Hawayo Takata, a woman born to Japanese parents in Hawaii, which had at that time just become a territory of the United States. This is not a biography of Takata herself, although she was a very interesting person. At the same time, Reiki in the West would be very different if it had not been introduced by Takata and if there had been no World War II. By looking at the history of a span of approximately 150 years, and the choices Hawayo Takata made in her lifetime, it is much easier to understand how Reiki – Real Reiki®, the intact

1

system fiercely guarded by Mrs. Takata until she found someone to whom to pass it – became available as it is today. The information included comes almost entirely from primary sources. Please feel free to ignore the endnotes if you prefer simply to read the story. The Bibliography also lists the wide range of source material used. The text notes where there is no evidence as to motive or if connections are speculative.

This book also draws from the many recorded hours of personal stories Hawayo Takata told to Dr. Barbara Ray in 1979, less than a year before Mrs. Takata's death. There are many stories about Reiki online written by people who have reinvented history, most of whom did not know Hawayo Takata personally. Almost forty years after Mrs. Takata's death, her voice is heard again in this book, in the historical context of the bigger picture.

1 WHAT IS REIKI?

If you are reading this book, you probably have heard the word "reiki." What you have heard, however, could be many things. A good beginning to this exploration of how Reiki came from Japan to the Western world is to start with what Reiki actually is.

The word "reiki" itself is made up of two Japanese words. It is not a real Japanese word. It was coined much the way in English we have the words "staycation" (a vacation while staying at home) or "doga" (yoga with dogs). In fact, in 1936 the word "reiki" was written in a Hawaiian Japanese-language newspaper in katakana characters, which is the alphabet used in Japanese writing for foreign words. For native speakers of Japanese, this usually indicates the word is not actually Japanese but rather a transliteration of the sounds from another language.

In Japanese, the word "rei" means universal or whole and the word "ki" refers to life-force energy. In other languages, "ki" is equivalent to "chi" or "qi" (Chinese), "prana" (Hindu), mana (Hawaiian Kahunas)[2], or "ruah" (Hebrew). Hawayo Takata, who brought the Japanese-named "reiki" system to the West, said that the Hindu equivalent term is "kana." In the rise of what is now called the "New Age" of the early 1970's, Mrs. Takata also talked to people exploring alternative techniques who equated the energy to "radionic waves." The idea of an energy which sustains life is named in many cultures. In the Star Trek universe, the writers even created the concept of the "pagh" in Bajoran religion to identify a non-material force within a being, similar to the Egyptian "ka."[3]

What differentiates Reiki from all the concepts of ki or chi or prana or mana is the addition of that word "rei." Combined with "rei," there is a connection to "ki" beyond the individual – *universal* life energy. Coining the word "Reiki" in Japanese indicated there is a larger or deeper meaning which transcends the basic concept of human life force.

Unfortunately, the word "reiki" is now a generic term. While it may have been coined to identify a specific method or technique more than a century ago, over time this specificity has been lost. There is more detail about how this happened in later chapters. For this discussion of what Reiki is, the word "Reiki" describes the real, intact system and not the multitude of things called "reiki" being offered in the twenty-first century.

One way to distinguish between many varied things called "reiki" and one specific technique is to use a different term. Real Reiki® is a service mark which was registered in 1983 to mean the actual, real technique taught by Hawayo Takata which she had been calling "reiki" all her life.

Mrs. Takata herself defined Reiki this way: "Reiki means universal life energy. It is a natural healing force [which] when applied, creates physical and mental harmony. It is a force that vitalizes your whole system... it is a useful aid to all things that has life."[4]

At the most basic, beginning level, Reiki is applied using the hands. On the one hand (no pun intended), this is helpful: most people have hands and can use them fairly easily. On the other hand, the outward appearance of someone placing their hands on themselves or someone else can get confused with a number of other types of things. Even though other things look similar from outside, there is an inner process which needs to be connected and in place.

In the intact system of Real Reiki®, once your hands have been activated by an Authorized Instructor who has been properly trained and connected to the intact system, any time you touch something living, you are bringing more universal life energy to that living system. Mrs. Takata was very clear that a connection had to be made and that she knew the way to do it. She said, "You buy a new TV, you have to plug in the socket and get the energy. I give my pupils the contact with the great universal life force...."[5]

Once you have a connection with the "great universal life force," what happens? When Mrs. Takata learned Reiki in Japan, she was very ill and was "cured" by Reiki treatments. In the 1930's in Japan, this was perfectly acceptable. In the West in the twenty-first century, there are stringent standards for medical healing and for claims of cures. It is true that at its deepest level, Reiki does promote healing... but we need a much wider perspective of what "healing" is.

In *The Reiki Factor*, the first book written about the intact system, Dr. Barbara Ray went into some detail about healing. As she wrote, the verb 'to heal' derives from an old English root meaning "to make whole."[6] With a wider sense of healing as "making whole," we can look at how Reiki works much more clearly, and get past the misleading medical associations.

How do you look at a person as a whole? One method is to use a model. With permission, the model created by Dr. Barbara Ray is reproduced on page 6.

In this model, the white center of the model represents that energy which is in everything alive. It could be called Light, or Spirit, or whole energy... the finest/clearest/lightest vibration in a living being. There are successively darker rings on the model to indicate denser or slower levels of

ENERGY MODEL

Vibrational Planes of Energy   Spectrum of Consciousness

Transforming – Wholing Process

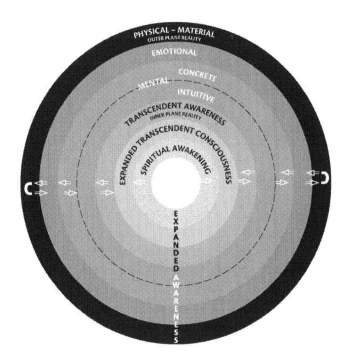

INNER TO OUTER
DENSITY TO ENLIGHTENMENT

energy within the same person, all existing simultaneously and vibrating together. The darkest – represented by the black outside ring – is the actual physical, material level. In a person, the physical body would include all the densities of bones, skin, blood, eyeballs, breath.... Each physical part has varying physical density (blood is a lot less dense than bone), but are represented in this model by the one black ring. The same thing applies to all the planes of energy represented in this Energy Model: each plane is made up of varying densities. For example, the emotional plane could include feelings of happiness, depression, silliness, boredom, all of these being types of emotions with varying densities or weight.

From the point of view of healing as making things whole, then, how would you limit *universal* energy to only one plane of energy? What if someone had cancer, was depressed about having cancer, and was extremely worried about the cost of treatment and needing to keep working to support his family? If that person got access to more universal energy, where would that energy be used to make things more whole (heal)? With Real Reiki®, the energy starts at the point of wholeness within that person and is used by that person's whole system *as that person needs it*. Real Reiki® offers *direct* access to universal energy, expanding that whole, universal energy to balance and align the entire body-mind-spirit dynamic. Fortunately, the practitioner does not need to make a decision about where the energy needs to go. In the example above, would you want the energy first to help reverse the actual cancer (physical), lift the depression (emotional) or ease the worrying (mental)? Who is arrogant enough to think they can make that kind of decision?

This mechanism of balancing the whole actually makes Real Reiki® extremely safe. The energy goes to where the system (person as a whole being) needs it. The practitioner does not have to concentrate or decide what needs more energy or where things are out of balance. Mrs. Takata always said "take care of the cause and the effect will come." The cause may not be something we know. However, the innate intelligence of the *whole* system does know what is out of balance, and can use universal energy to bring the energies of that whole system into alignment with the basic pattern of wholeness inherent to that system.

To address this concept another way, there is a blueprint of wholeness within each of us. The seed of a flower has encoded within it how that flower will grow. If you look at a sunflower seed, it is not obvious that if planted and watered, that seed will grow into a tall plant with a large yellow flower. Likewise, we can't look at a human being and see everything that human may grow and bloom into. The blueprint of that person – one part of which we have discovered in DNA – is encoded within.

Using the Energy Model as an image, we can posit the inner blueprint of a person as being encoded in that point of Light in the center. When that person gains access to more universal energy, it is as if the blueprint – the seed – is being given the equivalent of the sunflower's earth, water and sunshine. Just as with a flower, if you give the seed more nourishment, it becomes more of what it is innately encoded to be. If a sunflower has grown and then does not get water for a few days, the flower droops. Give it more water and it perks up again. It uses the water to get back to the way it normally would be, as its blueprint has the pattern.

However, there is a limit to physical recovery even just in terms of cellular capacity. In this example, after a certain point, the cells in the sunflower's stalk would have a very difficult time rehydrating to use water to rejuvenate the flower. They might have been dry for so long that they no longer would have the capacity to use the water as they had before. This shows that on the physical level there are real limits. This is a fair analogy of why Real Reiki® cannot *guarantee* physical healing. While the universal energy accessed by Real Reiki® will be used by the entire mind-body-spirit dynamic where it is needed, if physical parts of the body have gotten extremely far from the original inner pattern of wholeness over an extended time – such as with chronic conditions – it would take an enormous amount of energy to affect the very solid, dense physical plane and recover from months or years of physical imbalance or slow-growing dis-ease.

Reiki cannot be advertised as a cure for cancer, a way to keep someone from committing suicide, or a cure for dementia — that would be misleading and irresponsible.

Even in Mrs. Takata's autobiography, she said that she frequently would say to someone, "Let me see what I can do," rather than "I will heal you." Even though she did not have the education to put it in terms of an Energy Model, she was clear she was there to supply extra energy for a healing process: remove the cause or the block, and the person's natural tendency towards wholeness will blossom.

Today, teachers of Real Reiki® (also known as The Radiance Technique® or TRT®) choose the words about the intact system very carefully. Mrs. Takata herself sometimes referred to Reiki as "laying on of hands," probably because it looks like that and "laying on of hands" is a term associated with healing. However, Mrs. Takata did not have an extensive education. In the tradition of "laying on of hands," there is a religious component. The person laying their hands on someone has to have some kind of divine intercession or right to be able to heal. That healing has to come from God, and there are a variety of beliefs and requirements for both the person doing the healing and one receiving it. For example, in the Mormon tradition, healing using the laying-on-of-hands is restricted to men, who are the only ones who can be priests. As Dr. Barbara Ray differentiates it,

> "Since the beginning of organized religions, the 'laying-on-of-hands' has been a major approach to healing <u>disease</u>. This kind of healing requires adherence to specific belief systems. The Radiance Technique® is not a religion of any kind, is not a science of healing of disease, is not based on a belief system, and is not a system of intercession for another person. The Radiance Technique® is a cosmic vibratory science of universal energy for directly accessing, directing and expanding Radiant, Whole, Cosmic, Inner Energy."[7]

Again, Real Reiki® is not a kind of religion and does not require any kind of belief. In fact, babies and animals can both give and receive Real Reiki® using their hands (or paws or hooves). A large portion of Mrs. Takata's early practice was using Reiki with neighboring Hawaiian ranchers' animals. Her notes have page after page of stories about using Reiki with cows, pigs, horses, and even goldfish. Mrs. Takata also began her Reiki practice calling it "Reiki massage treatment."[8] At the time, this was the known acceptable way to do something in Hawaii which involved touching people. Mrs. Takata herself was clear that Reiki does not involve manipulation of any kind, although she also studied massage techniques. Into the 1960's, Mrs. Takata reported her Reiki income as "massage."[9] Today in the United States, a number of states require a massage license to accept money for touching someone in a TRT® Hands-on session, even if you are not actually doing manipulations. In some jurisdictions, even using TRT® without physically touching is also regulated. Licensed Authorized Instructors of The Radiance Technique® who choose to offer a professional TRT® Hands-on practice maintain the licenses appropriate to where they live.

Reiki can also be applied without the use of hands. Mrs. Takata often referred to "sending" energy to people. However, the actual process is better described as "directing." The word "sending" implies there is energy which starts with the practitioner and is sent over a distance like a package. "Directing" energy with the tools of Real Reiki® actually connects at that point of Light shown in the middle of the Energy Model and expands universal energy through the entire person. There is no energy being "sent" from "somewhere else."

The basic purpose of Real Reiki® is to access transcendental, universal energy. That energy can then be used by your entire body-mind-spirit dynamic in all circumstances. You can use Real Reiki® for everyday things. There are many practical things: put a hand over a cut; or use a free hand on your throat while talking on the telephone; or use hands-on to help recover at the end of a stressful day. Real Reiki® is also a tool to deepen meditation, enhance mindfulness practices, and, ultimately, activate from within the process of enlightenment.

One of the most important points in any discussion about what Real Reiki® is, is how it is activated. Again, Mrs. Takata was always clear that there needed to be an activation process, and that she knew how to set up the connection. She did not say much about how it was actually done. From her earliest interviews, though, she made it clear there was a process and she knew how to do it.

If you have a house and you need a new light switch installed, you know there is a way it needs to be done. The light switch has to be put into the wall, wired so that it has access to electricity, and that source of electricity has to be connected to a source (the grid, a battery or a solar panel). You need someone who knows the process in order to get it done. It is relatively easy to know whether your new light switch was installed correctly: turn it on and the light should come on.

What Mrs. Takata knew – the science of Real Reiki® – is similar to the process of installing the light switch. There is a sequence of steps which need to be done so that when you put your hand on (or near) a living thing, energy expands from the point of light within that living thing. Someone who has been properly trained AND who has the key to accessing the source/point of light (as the person installing the light switch connects it to the electrical source) can set up the "switch" for another person. Someone who does not have the training or never had the key is not capable of setting up the "switch." Similarly, someone who copied bits of the key but has no connection also cannot set up the "switch." It would be as if someone got a piece of an electrical diagram and tried to connect wires to make it look like the two-dimensional diagram... but there was no connection to a source of electricity.

In the science of Real Reiki®, the processes which set up that "light switch" are called Attunements or alignment processes. "Attune" is used like tuning in a radio station or setting the preset channel in your car. Once the correct Attunement process has been done, the switch works every time, whether you are thinking about it, are tired, ate breakfast, have shoes on, or any other variations of the outer planes. This is another reason Real Reiki® is so safe: it does not depend upon the condition of the person doing hands-on.

Almost forty years after Mrs. Takata's death and more than eighty years after Mrs. Takata began offering Reiki in Hawaii, the origins of the science in modern times certainly do not affect anyone using this science. However, there is a legend about how this particular ancient technique was rediscovered for the modern day: the legend of Dr. Usui, presented in the next chapter.

2 THE ORIGINS OF REIKI

Hawayo Takata, a young woman in the Hawaiian islands in the 1930's, became the first person to use Reiki in the Western Hemisphere in modern times. Mrs. Takata herself first learned Reiki in Japan. However, her information about the background of the technique itself in Japan came from stories and comments which she heard and then recounted years later. These stories became the part of the legend of Reiki for many decades. Even when Mrs. Takata herself began to write a book about Reiki in the 1970's, she gave variations of what she had been saying since the 1940's, which had become a legend rather than a factual and documented explanation.

The legend is that Reiki was rediscovered by a Japanese man named Mikao Usui. Mrs. Takata wrote the story in one of her book drafts this way[10]:

"Dr. Mikao Usui was a Christian minister, also Principal of Doshisha University, Kyoto, Japan. .... He became a Zen student and there he found in the Sutras that Buddha healed. He was looking for a formula, he went deep into Chinese characters, for Buddhism came into Japan from China, Korea to Japan. He became a master of Chinese culture, but he said this is not enough — He studied Sanskrit,

Buddha was born in India — In Sanskrit he found the formulas, art of Healing — he rejoiced, now he had to test it, for it was so long, long ago that it was written — 2,500 years. According to his findings, Buddha expressed that it was God Power, when God created this Universe, he left the Universal Life energy to be used and applied to mankind and all things that have life shall benefit. I do not know much about Dr. Usui, it is hearsay from my Master Teacher Chijiro Hayashi, I met in the fall of 1935. Dr. Usui had long ago went into transition."

Before World War II, in a 1939 article about the opening of her new Reiki office in Hilo, Mrs. Takata presented the history of Reiki much more simply. According to this article, Mrs. Takata "was the first one to bring the art to Hawaii since it had been jealously guarded in Japan for the last 3,000 years."[11]

In 1980, Mrs. Takata also told a lengthy story about Usui to a small group of students in Atlanta with a tape recorder running. The outlines are the same, but she includes many colorful details. In this version of the legend, Dr, Usui also started as a Christian minister, but Mrs. Takata creates the scene:

"One day on a Sunday he [Dr. Usui] was at the podium giving Sunday service or lecture. And that day he found about a half-dozen students on the front pew. Usually the students of the university sit in the back. Then he [Dr. Usui] said, "Good morning, everybody. I am ready to deliver our Sunday sermon."

The students challenged him, asking about his faith, and saying,

"'Please give us one demonstration.' And Dr. Usui said, 'What kind of demonstration?' [The student] said, 'We would like to see you heal the blind, or heal the lame, or walk on the waters. The way it happened in the Bible.'"

As Mrs. Takata continues the story, Dr. Usui was taken aback. He really didn't know how those things had happened and had just taken the stories on faith. In her story, Dr. Usui said,

"'Tomorrow being Monday, I shall stop [teaching] and I shall go to a Christian country to study the Bible... and I might find the answer. And when I do, I shall come back and shall let you know what I can do that you requested.' He said good-bye and he left the church."[12]

Dr. Mikao Usui (undated photo)

The legend continues that Dr. Usui obtained a visa to go to America and went to study at the University of Chicago. Again, this is part of Mrs. Takata's story. In 1983, the American-International Reiki Association sent an official request for information to the University of Chicago. The

Registrar certified that they had no record of any student named Dr. Mikao Usui attending the university since its founding in 1891.[13]

In Mrs. Takata's story, after seven years studying the world's religions (not only Christianity), Dr. Usui decided to return to Japan and explore Buddhism. As Mrs. Takata told it, he visited almost every temple in Japan and asked about their healing techniques. The story goes on:

"After days and days and months of search, Dr. Usui was very depressed. But he did not give up. He said, 'I have one more place to go.' Finally he landed in a Zen Temple. And when he approached the temple, he rang the temple and a little page boy came out. He said, 'I would like to speak to the highest monk of this temple.' 'Please, come in. Who are you?' 'I am Mikao Usui and I would like to study Buddhism.' The message was delivered. When the monk came out he was about seventy-two years old monk, a very lovely face like a child, very innocent looking, beautiful face, kindly voice and very gentle."[14]

This has to be Mrs. Takata embroidering for dramatic effect: it seems very unlikely that Dr. Hayashi would have conveyed that level of detail to Mrs. Takata forty years earlier. Again, as recounted by Mrs. Takata, Dr. Usui studied Buddhism at this temple for three years. While he kept studying the Japanese sutras, he felt this was not enough. Finally he consulted the same monk, who told him:

"'The Japanese characters that is written [sic] in the sutras, all these characters... originally came from China. We have adopted the Chinese characters as Japanese characters. And so when you read the sutras, you cannot understand.' [A parenthetical explanation here by Mrs. Takata: "You cannot understand, but it is like English people reading Latin. Characters are read as written."] He could do it. So finally he went very deeply into the Chinese characters, and became a master at reading these

Chinese characters. The monk said, 'Not enough. After all, Buddha was a Hindu, and therefore you should study the Sanskrit, and if you study the Sanskrit there may be something in [the] Sanskrit notes by the Buddha's disciples. Buddha had many, many disciples...' And so he [Usui] went to study the Sanskrit, he studied hard to master it, he found the formula, nothing hard, very simple such as 2 + 2 = 4, 3 + 3 = 6, as simple as this. 'Very well,' he said, 'I have found it. But now I have to try to interpret this. Because it was written 2,500 years ago, ancient.' He said, 'I don't know if this will work or not. But I will have to go through this test. I will not guarantee myself if I will live through it or not. But if I don't try the test, everything will be lost. We will go back to zero.'"[15]

At that point the legend moves on to Dr. Usui traveling to a mountain to meditate for twenty-one days:

"He said he expected some kind of a phenomena, he didn't know what to expect. All this time he very faithfully read the sutras, meditated and chanted. ...Finally came the morning of the twenty-first [day]. And he said, 'The darkest of the night is in the earliest of morning before the sunrise.' There was not even one star or moon. The sky was dark as it could be. And when he finished his meditation and looked into the vast sky and all he was thinking, 'This is my last meditation.' And then he saw a flicker of light, only as large as a candle light in the dark sky.... And the light started to move very fast towards him. And he said, 'Oh, the light. Now I have a choice to shirk the light or to dodge? What shall I do?' Then he said, 'Even if the light strikes me and if I fall and the contact is severe, I might drop or I might go. This is the test.' He said, 'I am not going to run away, I am going to face the light.'... With that, he relaxed, and with his eyes wide open he saw the light strike him in the center of his forehead. And naturally... it forced him backwards because the force was so great. But then he said, 'I died, I had no feeling, no sense. I could not see, but my eyes were shut. I don't know how long, how many minutes I had died.'"[16]

The rest of the legend explains how Dr. Usui started to share what he had discovered. This is when Japanese rules and customs were created around what was an ancient formula for accessing universal life energy.

Some modern "reiki" practitioners claim to have found Dr. Usui's grave in Japan, and today generally tend to say he died in 1922 (although there are other dates depending on the sources). This claim of finding a grave appeared after Mrs. Takata's death and differs from Mrs. Takata's story of Dr. Usui living in the mid-1800's.

Fortunately, when exactly Dr. Usui lived and the exact story behind his rediscovery of Reiki are irrelevant to the real story of Reiki in the Western world. By 1935, Dr. Usui was no longer alive, whether he died in 1922 or another year. Hawayo Takata did go to Japan and did meet and study with Dr. Chujiro Hayashi. There is ample evidence of Mrs. Takata's visits to Japan and Dr. Hayashi's extensive stay in Hawaii, along with his certification of Takata herself. The technique undoubtedly had power and was being used in a standardized way in Japan when Takata was introduced to it. Exactly when and how someone (Dr. Usui or someone else) codified the system called "Reiki" in Japan is a topic for a different book.

Dr. Barbara Ray, a Ph.D. in Classics and Art History who had made a lifelong study of Latin and Ancient Civilizations, had long studied ancient sacred systems. She recognized what Mrs. Takata called "Reiki" as one of the ancient healing systems and tools to gain inner knowledge which are referenced in classical sources. In the first book ever published about the science, *The Reiki Factor*[17], Dr. Ray wrote, "Throughout its long history, the knowledge of what is called in modern times 'Reiki' has been passed from teacher to student by word of mouth. The origins of Reiki can be found in ancient Tibet many, many thousands of years ago."[18] From her knowledge of classics, Dr. Ray traced the science from India into different forms in Egypt, Greece, Rome, and through China and Japan. The science had different outer forms. However, each intact system had specific methods, like installing a light switch in the earlier analogy, for activating "circuits" in humans to use and apply a higher source of energy reliably and consistently.

In the 1930's in Japan, one of these intact systems was available and was called Reiki. Hawayo Takata brought this technique to the West. As she said in 1980,

"...my followers and students have learned this system as The Usui Reiki Ryoho. Of course this is Japanese, so in English I have called it The Usui System in the Art of Healing. In Japanese it is Reiki, but in English it is universal Life-energy. But I use it as Reiki because I learned in Japan and therefore I continue to say it in the shorter word as Reiki."[19]

Today this intact system is referred to in English using a number of different phrases, including The Radiance Technique®, Authentic Reiki®, Real Reiki®, and Radiant Touch®, with other terms being used in other languages (Die Radiance Technik®, Technica Radianta®). TRT® is another term which is not as language-specific. All of these phrases are registered as service marks to refer to the technique Hawayo Takata brought to the Western world as simply the Japanese term "Reiki."

3 JAPANESE IN HAWAII

While Reiki as an ancient sacred science is not inherently Japanese, Mrs. Takata brought Reiki to the West from Japan. She herself was born to Japanese parents. That background and the position of the Japanese in Hawaii had a great influence on how Mrs. Takata presented Reiki throughout her life.

The islands which make up Hawai'i floated in the Pacific Ocean for centuries as an autonomous kingdom. Occasional ships discovered the islands, with the possibility of a Japanese fishing vessel having been wrecked on Maui as early as five hundred years before the explorer Captain Cook arrived in 1778.[20] From the time of Cook's landing, a variety of Western businessmen began growing and exporting sugar from the robust sugar cane crop. However, the islands remained fairly isolated until the 1850's. As far as a Japanese connection goes, in 1850, a total of three Japanese men from a number of shipwrecked Japanese crews had settled in the Kingdom of Hawaii and become subjects, while the rest of the Japanese who had visited all had returned to Japan.[21] In the meantime, the approximately 300,000 Hawaiians who had lived on the islands when Captain Cook first arrived in 1778 had been decimated by Western diseases to about 70,000 native Hawaiians in 1850.[22]

From the time of Captain Cook, a number of Westerners discovered the profitability of Hawaii as a source of sugar cane to meet the Western world's demand for sugar. Sugar cane grew very well on the islands. Entrepreneurial (or rapacious) Westerners took over large swathes of land for large-scale production. After an unsuccessful attempt to import plantation labor from China, in 1868 the Hawaiian consul general in Yokohama, Eugene Van Reed, arranged for the first group of Japanese immigrants to Hawaii. The general feeling at the time was that Japanese people would fit into the Hawaiian culture and race, as expressed by a politician to the Hawaiian Chamber of Commerce in 1872:

> "We must look to races, who whilst being good workers, will not much affect the identity of the Hawaiian, and whose gradual influx will harmonize with, and strengthen, by the infusion of new blood, the native stock. A moderate portion of the Japanese, of the agricultural class, will not conflict with the view that I present, and if they bring their women with them, and settle permanently in the country, they may be counted upon as likely to become desirable Hawaiian subjects."[23]

The United States and Hawaii signed a reciprocity agreement in 1876 which allowed Hawaiian sugar to be imported duty-free into the U.S. A large number of Japanese soon immigrated to Hawaii, mainly to work on the sugar cane plantations. This move was so successful that a journal for plantation owners reported in 1888 about the Japanese workers,

> "These people assume so readily the customs and habits of the country, that there does not exist the same prejudice against them that there is with the Chinese, while as laborers they seem to give as much satisfaction as any others."[24]

The Japanese population in Hawaii expanded very quickly. In 1884, the Hawaiian census reported 116 Japanese residents. Sixteen years later there were 47,508 Japanese men and 13,603 Japanese women.[25] The majority of immigrants were contract laborers from Hiroshima and Yamaguchi, which are provinces in the southwestern part of Japan. The immigrants were mostly from rural villages and were accustomed to marrying early and having many children who would then help them on the plantations. One of the immigrants from Yamaguchi Province was Otogoro Kawamura.

Hawayo Takata always said that her father "came as an infant."[26] Otogoro was born in 1867, according to his own reporting in the 1910 census, although later in life he claimed to be a bit younger.[27] If he had come to Hawaii as an infant, he would have had to have been one of the first group of Japanese to arrive: the first group in 1868 consisted of just 140 men, six women and two children.[28] However, as is evident in a number of instances, Mrs. Takata loved to tell a good story. According to what Otogoro reported on the 1930 census, which probably is closer to the truth, he immigrated in 1891. There is a ship's manifest dated January 9, 1892 which lists a 24-year-old Otogoro Kawamura as a passenger.

Otogoro settled on the garden island of Kauai and began working for the Makee Sugar Company. The background of Makee Sugar presents an intriguing window into some of the early Western settlement of Hawaii. The characters involved also had a profound impact later on the young Hawayo's life.

In 1843, Captain James Makee, a New England sailor, was almost killed by his ship's cook (who violently attacked him with a cleaver) while off the coast of Hawaii. During his recovery and convalescence, Makee became extremely interested in Hawaii. Moving his wife and family from Massachusetts to Honolulu, he became a prominent Hawaiian settler, first succeeding in the whaling industry and then in trade, ranching, and sugar. He purchased plantation land on several islands, growing sugar cane and raising horses and cattle. During the U.S. Civil War, Captain

Makee made a generous "patriotic gift" of two 100-barrel donations of molasses.[29] After a number of successful business ventures, in 1878 Makee also went into partnership with Hawaii's King Kalakaua, buying the Kealia Plantation in Kapaa, Kauai as a part of the recently-formed Makee Sugar corporation.

Lihue Village, Kauai in 1887, showing the Lihu'e Plantation sugar mill, camp housing, and Nawiliwili Stream

Captain Makee died in 1879 at the age of 67 with eight children still living. His daughter, Wilhelmina, had married an even more colorful man, Colonel Zephaniah Swift Spalding, son of a judge in Ohio. Colonel Spalding had first made a name for himself during the U.S. Civil War, ending his war service as commander of the Twenty-seventh Regiment of Ohio volunteers. After the war he was sent to Hawaii as a advance agent for the State Department[30] and in 1867 was appointed by President Andrew Johnson as United States Consul to Hawaii.[31] He represented both the original Hawaiian monarchy at the Exposition Universelle of Paris in

1889 and then in 1898, under the new government, was Chargé d'Affaires for the Hawaiian Legation in Belgium. Colonel Spalding also procured a franchise in 1895 for laying the first communications cable between Hawaii and San Francisco. The Hawaiian subsidy was $40,000 per year while the cost of laying the cable ended up being approximately $3,000,000.[32] Opening up this ready communication with the mainland had a profound impact on the development of the islands.

After Captain Makee's death in 1879, Colonel Spalding purchased a controlling interest in the Makee Sugar Co. and eventually bought out King Kalakaua as well. By 1914, a description of the Makee Sugar Company in a local paper read:

"The Makee Sugar Company, Ltd. is an Hawaiian corporation, its plantation and mill being located around Kapaa and Kealia, the latter being the post office. R. P. Spalding is president, G. P. Wilcox vice-president, and The Spalding Co., of Los Angeles, treasurer. Although his name does not appear in this list, it is generally understood that Colonel Z. S. Spalding is practically the owner of the plantation. It is an irrigated estate, the various parts being connected by railway. The sugar output for 1914 was 9935 tons, which was considerably above the estimate, due to exceptionally favorable weather conditions."[33]

The Spalding family was one to be reckoned with. Quoting from a California newspaper, the Kauai newspaper, *The Garden Island*, reprinted the following in 1912:

"One of the richest individual land owners in the world is Col. Z. S. Spalding, the Hawaiian sugar magnate, who owns the great 11,000-acre Spalding tract south of Willows. He owns a ranch near Rome, Italy, of several thousand acres. In Canada, he has 60,000 acres in one tract. He owns 10,000 acres in Butte and Tehama Counties. It is said he owns land on every great division of the earth, many thousand acres of which are in Asia. In the Hawaiian Islands he has 4000 acres of the finest sugar cane land in the world."[34]

Despite this (or perhaps because he pursued interests in so many places outside of Hawaii), Colonel Spalding and Makee Sugar were not even one of the so-called Big Five which controlled the majority of the sugar production in Hawaii.

Politically, the Hawaiian islands saw much upheaval and change at the end of the nineteenth century. On January 17, 1893, a consortium of American residents overthrew the legitimate royal Hawaiian government. The overthrowing of the monarchy may well have been inspired at least in part by sugar interests, although the planters themselves were for the most part not involved in the takeover.[35] Labor at this time also became more organized, with the first major sugar cane strike in 1897. Negotiations to make Hawaii a United States territory were brokered by a broad group of politicians, businessmen, and others after the Hawaiian monarchy was deposed. In 1898 Hawaii was annexed to the United States, and in 1900 the islands officially became a U.S. territory.

However, none of these earthshaking events had much impact on plantation families. Harvest and processing continued, especially on the islands further from the big island of Hawaii and the bureaucratic centers on Oahu. The influx of farmers for the plantations had brought a corresponding need for women to marry these farmers. By the mid-1890's, quite a few Japanese women were seeking their fortunes in the beautiful climate of the Hawaiian islands.

In 1894, a young woman named Hatsu Tamashima immigrated to the Hawaiian Kingdom from Kagawa, Japan. She was born sometime between 1863 and 1875 (as with Otogoro, the self-reported age varies through their lives), so she was most likely already in her twenties, which was fairly old for a farmer's wife. Otogoro Kawamura and Hatsu Tamashima married on February 2, 1897.

The Kawamuras had their first child, a daughter, less than a year after their marriage. As Hawayo Takata told it, the daughter was named

> "'Kawayo,' after Kauai. But she only lived ten days or so and she passed on. And my mother said, 'This child wasn't sick. But she didn't like her name. Her name was too small, so that is why she didn't live long!'"[36]

Next they had a son, Kazuo, who would serve in the U.S. Army during World War I and then die young, in 1920.

Almost three years later, the Kawamuras had another little girl, on the morning of December 24, 1900. Mrs. Takata said, "And my mother asked the midwife, 'Is it a boy or a girl?' And the midwife said, 'It is a baby girl — black hair, and very, very strong child.'"[37] Hawaii had become a territory six months previously. Since the first girl's name "Kawayo" was too small, Hatsu decided this girl would be called "Hawayo" after the entire territory of Hawaii. "And so she said success not only in Kauai but in the territory of Hawaii, not knowing that in many, many later years that we would ever become a state."[38] Mrs. Takata was very proud throughout her lifetime that she was born the year Hawaii became a territory, and then that Hawaii became a state. In fact, she owned a first-day postal issue from the day Hawaii became a state, postmarked August 21, 1959 at 10 a.m.

We know of three more Kawamura sisters and possibly another brother, all born between 1904 and 1913. Given the rates of infant mortality, there may well have been other children who did not survive to be reported on a census. By 1913, Hatsu could also have been well into her forties, depending on which birthdate is correct. Hawayo Takata herself wrote of her father supporting a family of two boys and five girls.

The Kawamura parents, Otogoro and Hatsu, never learned to read or write. They were listed throughout their lives as being Japanese speakers, while their children all spoke English. Hawayo and her siblings all attended school and learned both Japanese and English, becoming educated far beyond their parents and fulfilling the promise of a better life in America.

When Hawaii became a territory, all children born in Hawaii also automatically became U.S. citizens, which made all the Kawamura children American citizens. They had ongoing cultural ties to Japan (and dual citizenship unless they applied to renounce it[39]), but they considered themselves Americans.

Listening to the tapes Hawayo Takata made for her autobiography late in her life, you can hear her very distinctive Japanese-Hawaiian accent and the rhythm of the language she heard growing up, which was not quite standard English as spoken in the continental United States. Her life embodies her combination of Japanese heritage and ways of thinking with American curiosity and conviction that she was capable of doing anything.

4 THE YOUNG HAWAYO

Hawayo Takata shared a fair amount about her early life in all of her autobiography drafts.[40] Certainly her background was foreign to most of those she talked to, especially in the 1970's as she finally became more public about her life and Reiki. While this is not a complete biography of Hawayo Takata (as intriguing a woman as she was, succeeding in life as a young Japanese widow in Hawaii through and after World War II), how she spent her earlier life informs and illuminates some of the choices she made later.

Life on Hawaiian sugar plantations, as in many farming communities, was geared towards as many people working the fields as possible. Children of plantation workers were expected to go into the fields as soon as they were able. The pay they earned went towards augmenting the family income.

Hawayo Takata and her siblings attended the public school "like all the children of our village." In the summer of 1913, when she was twelve, Hawayo began working in the cane fields along with all her classmates. As she told it[41],

"all the cane cutters would go out and cut the cane
in this great big field and then we would take about
a foot, about twelve inches, from the top and we

would cut them and we fill up a gunny sack. And we have our numbers, and that was our identification. And we were paid about thirteen cents a bag [$3.36 in 2019 dollars[42]], which was very, very good wages. So during the summer all the able students went into the fields to work."

Harvesting Sugar Cane (1912)

Hawayo was very short, rather "delicate" (her word) and not very strong, so she ran into problems doing this work. "So when the supervisor came and shook the bag out it became three-fourths, and I was heartbroken and disappointed. And so, like a child, I cried. It was so distressing." Two family friends who were in the field saw her. They told her,

"You should not come out here to work because you are too young. You should be home playing with mud-pies and dolls. You are too young to work in the cane field. It is impossible for you to carry that bag or to fill it up is a very, very hard thing. But since you have courage to come out and you are trying very hard, don't cry. We will help you. We will cut our lunch hour short and we will come and cut

30

the cane tops and we will fill the bag for you.... Fill them up as much as you can, but otherwise just leave the gunny sacks and pile up the cane tops and go with the rest of the gang."

The friends continued to help Hawayo like this all summer.

At the beginning of the next school year, the school could not find a second substitute teacher for the first-grade class. Hawayo was a good student, the principal liked her, and they asked her whether she would be willing to fill in. She would turn thirteen in December. After getting permission from her father, she accepted. She said she was paid "a five-dollar gold piece and a silver dollar on Friday. And that was a very, very great help to the family." That position also meant she did not need to go back to the cane fields the next summer, and, as it turned out, ever again.

In 1914, still working as a substitute teacher – which sounds as if it may have been more a teaching assistant, since she comments that the students liked her, as if she worked with them every day – the plantation opened what they called the Emporium. There was a grand opening. Hawayo walked miles to the opening:

"When I went to the opening of this store, there was a man who had a concession to a soda fountain. And so he came and said 'Oh, Hawayo, what are you doing here?' I said, 'Just like everybody else, I came to the opening of this Emporium.' 'Do you know what you can do?' I said, 'What can I do for you?' He said, 'Come over the counter and wash the dishes. I have the concession to the soda fountain. And then I will make the chocolate sundae, and strawberry sundae, and ice cream sodas, so there will be many, many guests and customers. So perhaps after washing the dishes you may be able to help me serve them.' So I said, 'I will be most happy to help you in any way I can.' And so I helped him until 5 o'clock. And he said, 'Don't walk home, because I will drive you home in my buggy.' And so after cleaning the soda fountain he took me home. He said to my father and my mother, 'Your daughter helped me today, and I was very, very fortunate. But now I see that I need a full-time girl. Do you think you could let Hawayo have that job? I think she is very, very capable and she learns very fast. And I would love to have her work at my soda fountain.'"[43]

After some discussion, her parents agreed to let Hawayo work on Saturdays only while she was still in school. She did not say whether this was at the end of the year she was fourteen, although other evidence tends to confirm she stopped going to school within the next year or so. When she finished school, she "still attended Japanese school from 6 to 8 in the morning and then I walked 7 miles to my full-time job."

After a while, the Emporium asked Hawayo to file papers and receipts in her spare time. This was her first introduction to bookkeeping, and became a very useful skill in later years. One day, when she was a full-time employee at the Emporium, a very elegant woman arrived with her chauffeur to order groceries. Hawayo helped her with her list and did a good job. After the woman left, the head of the grocery department praised her work and told Hawayo the woman was a very important customer, and a countess.

Each time the countess came to the store, Hawayo greeted her and helped fill her order. Finally, as Hawayo Takata recounted it, one day the countess came in and they had a conversation:

"She said, 'Little girl, do you ever have a vacation?' I said, 'Yes, ma'am, I have a vacation one week a year.' So she said, 'Will you come to my house when you have your vacation? Because you said to me that your father is working in Kealia and not in [inaudible] and you are staying at the church boarding house, and then you are coming here to work. I can give you a job right here in my home. I would love to have you, and your father and mother would be very happy, too, I am sure, because you can visit them and stay a whole day every Sunday. And if you will come, I will double your wages, whatever you are making here, and also dress you and give you room and board.' She made it very, very attractive."[44]

Hawayo decided to tell her boss about this and ask his advice. He was quite willing to have her visit on her vacation. As Hawayo said he put it, "We do not like to let you go, but this is our business. We have to please our customers and she is one of our biggest customers." He agreed to give Hawayo a recommendation if she wanted to move on. When she told this story, she was clear she was concerned about giving up her good job for an unknown situation. Having the recommendation from the store gave her an option if things did not work out.[45]

The countess was actually Countess Alice Makee Spalding Bonzi, one of Colonel Zephaniah Spalding's daughters and a granddaughter of Captain Makee of Makee Sugar. Her nickname was "Flibby." Alice Makee Spalding was born on Kauai in 1879 and raised in Hawaii, California and Italy. In a grand ceremony in her father's house on Kauai in March 1903, she married the Italian Count Leonardo Ercole Bonzi.[46] While Count Bonzi's mother, who was not well, lived in Rome, the Count's home was in Crema near Milan. They also kept a house in Kauai and later another one in Napa, California.

When Hawayo visited Countess Bonzi, she was first introduced to the cook and then given a tour of the estate.

"The estate was about one hundred acres, twelve acres in house lot [*Ed.: the house section covered twelve acres*], and had five cottages, a big stable, and of course the main mansion, a very stately-looking colonial type. Of course, I have never seen such mansions in my past life. So everything looked very, very elegant. And then a Japanese woman gently persuaded me to stay. And she said, 'It's a nice place to work and the work is not hard. Perhaps you will have longer hours, but the pay is very good. And of course she said she will dress you up. But you will not wear any dresses, perhaps only at home. But while you are here you are going to be dressed in Kimono and Obi in a very elegant style.'... I said, 'You know very well I can't afford to buy this.' And she said, 'No, but I am sure the lady is going to dress you.' And of course that made me very, very happy."[47]

Hawayo's parents saw the advantages to this job, both in seeing her every weekend and her earning twice as much money. Hawayo was probably only fifteen or so, and the family had younger children still at home. There is some mention of her living at the church boarding house by this time, so she was ready to move to a residential job.

The connection with Countess Bonzi lasted for twenty-four years. "...From waitress, pantry girl, I was promoted to number one housekeeper. And because I had little knowledge about figures, I could handle her twenty-one servants, paychecks and supervise. And I enjoyed every moment."[48] Countess Alice Bonzi died in California in 1949, so that twenty-four years was probably the rest of the Countess's life.

There are no written records about Hawayo's personal life, and she does not explain the exact sequence of many events. However, since she was living in proximity to the Spalding family who owned the Makee Sugar Company, it seems likely this created the opportunity for Hawayo to meet the assistant bookkeeper for Makee Sugar, Saichi Takata.

In the 1914 newspaper listing of sugar companies' salaried employees and officers[49], the post of Makee Sugar assistant bookkeeper was held by S. Takata. Saichi was born in 1895, only five years before Hawayo. In 1914 he would have been barely nineteen. His was also the only Japanese name on the Makee list, and one of the few Japanese in salaried positions for any of the Kauai Sugar companies listed. In the Makee roster, with the exception of two Chinese-sounding names for the Sugar Boiler positions, everyone else sounds Western.

Hawayo Kawamura and Saichi Takata married on March 10, 1917, at most two years after they may have first met. He was twenty-one; she was sixteen. He was the respected assistant bookkeeper of the Makee Sugar Co. and a cashier at the Kealia Store (probably the official name of the Emporium). She had a good position at Countess Bonzi's house.

Newspaper records about Saichi Takata reveal a diligent, responsible young man. Although he did not end up serving in the military in World War I, he was number 623 on the official draft list for Kauai. In 1918, the Red Cross sponsored a special war-effort blood drive, and Saichi was one of the volunteers coordinating in Kealia. In September 1918, both he and Hawayo, individually, were on the Honor Roll of Fourth Liberty Loan.

Saichi had brought the younger Japanese men of the Kealia plantation together in March 1918 to form a local chapter of the Young Men's Buddhist Association (Y.M.B.A.). The purpose of the Y.M.B.A. in Hawaii was to help new immigrants adjust to society and learn English, and "give religious training and solace."[50] On the first day, the new Y.M.B.A. chapter sold $135 in war savings stamps to support the war effort ($2290 in 2019 dollars).[51] Mrs. Takata's exposure to the Y.M.B.A. may have also given her some of the tactics she used later to make Reiki seem acceptable to Americans.

The young Takata couple appeared to settle into a happy married life. Their first daughter, Julia Sayoko, was born in 1919, followed by Alice Emiko in 1925. Again, while Mrs. Takata did not include this kind of detail in her autobiographies, Julia Makee Spalding Senni was the Countess' older sister, who also married an Italian count. Of course, the countess herself was named Alice. It seems very unlikely that the Takatas just coincidentally gave their daughters the English names "Julia" and "Alice."

In the 1920's, the couple participated in various aspects of island life. In 1922 Saichi played the role of "Jino Teno" in a highly-acclaimed pageant at a Legion Dance. Other roles in the pageant included the Spirit of the East; ladies-in-waiting representing India, Japan, China and Egypt; a "Hindoo" soldier; fan bearers; Aladdin; Ptolomey; and a number of others. The newspaper commented, "Any one who missed the Legion's dance Saturday evening without doubt missed one of the most enjoyable affairs ever presented on Kauai."[52]

Saichi also seems to have introduced Hawayo to golf, a sport which she played regularly and competitively her entire life. Saichi competed in November 1921 in the very first handicap tournament held by the newly-formed Wailua Golf Club, and came in second. He had 64 actual and his 18 handicap brought him down to 46.[53]

Mrs. Takata submitted a recipe to the *Honolulu Star-Bulletin* recipe contest, and while it did not win, the newspaper reprinted it among those that "were almost as good as those that won prizes." The following was printed in the group of "recipes for vegetables." Apparently in 1926 this counted as a vegetable recipe:

Italian Spaghetti

1 cup grated cheese, 3 cups chopped cold roast or steak, 1 cup sugar corn (canned), 1 cup olive oil, 1 tin tomato paste (small), ¼ pound spaghetti, 1 cup onions chopped together with garlic.

Heat olive oil in frying pan, put in chopped onions, cook about five minutes, put in tomato paste, meat, corn and season with salt, paprika and pepper. Mix this mixture with spaghetti, butter a baking dish and bake for 15 minutes. Sprinkle the cheese between layers and on top. Serve with plain rice.[54]

Anyone who had contact with Mrs. Takata after she started to offer Reiki would receive her strong recommendations about healthy diet and good foods as an essential component of health. As a contrast to her Italian Spaghetti, here is what many years later she called "Reiki Slaw:"

1 head of white cabbage
1 head of cauliflower
2 medium-sized raw beets
4 stalks of celery, diced
Grate the first three ingredients, add in the diced celery and season to taste.[55]

Saichi Takata continued to take on responsibilities as he matured. He served on the Kauai child welfare board, and according to Mrs. Takata was the first "Oriental" to be named to that board. In April 1930, he was one of two chairmen coordinating the dedication of the Spalding Monument. Colonel Spalding had died in 1927. The Japanese on the Kealia plantation erected a monument to Spalding at the "junction of the main government road and The Valley House road, two miles above Kealia."[56] At the dedication service, Saichi gave a speech about Colonel Spalding's life. Interestingly, another man gave a Japanese translation of Saichi's speech.

Saichi died suddenly on October 7, 1930. Mrs. Takata did not really say what he died of, except that it was not expected. On the other hand, Saichi had traveled to Japan in 1928 to consult his friend, a famous surgeon. The doctor was Tomosuke Maeda, who in 1927 founded the Maeda Hospital. The hospital is still in business today.[57] Whatever his medical issues, Saichi continued all his regular activities and, from the records available, no one thought he was going to die at that time.

In the tapes Mrs. Takata made at the end of her life, hoping all the material would become a book, she dedicated her book to the "memory of my beloved husband, Saichi Takata." Then she continued,

"This is the preface and I would like to say a few things about my beloved husband. When he passed into transition on October 7, 1930 he was only 34 years of age. But before his transition, three days, he talked about his funeral. And so he said, 'Understand that nothing remains the same. The law of the universe is change. And why, if I go all of a sudden,' he said, 'I do not want you to be shocked. I do not want you to grieve over this.'"[58]

Mrs. Takata said of her process of finding Reiki,
"It was not accidental, but many, many sorrows passed into my path of life.... In late 1919 [my father] had an accident which crushed his left hand, he could not save his thumb. Before this was completely healed, my older brother, who served in the World War I, was honorably discharged. [He] worked in the sugar mill... helping the family. He died of flu. He was 23 years old. Before our tears dried, a sister went into transition March 16th 1922 — she was 18. It was another shock to the family. I witnessed 6 funerals from 1920 to 1930 — that is when I became a widow at 29 years old. What a sad family."[59]

After Saichi's death, Hawayo Takata was a young widow with two daughters, ages twelve and five. Ten years before, upon her brother's death, Hawayo had become the oldest child in the family. With her father's hand injury, she was also the one who was most qualified and fit to be the family breadwinner.

Initially Hawayo seems to have filled in for Saichi in a number of ways. In January 1931, she was appointed and approved as Kawaihau water collector.[60] According to her autobiography, that was a job with pay. Months after Saichi's death, another source of income was welcome to support her family.

In July 1932, Mrs. Hawayo Takata joined twelve others of the various Hawaiian chapters of Y.M.B.A. (Young Men's

Buddhist Association) to participate in the Canada-Hawaii-America Y.M.B.A. Conference in San Francisco. The group also added a side excursion to attend the 1932 Los Angeles Summer Olympics.[61] Her involvement in the Y.M.B.A. presumably began during Saichi's lifetime.

While the mission of the Y.M.B.A. began as a cognate to the YMCA (Young Men's Christian Association) and a way to help immigrants establish themselves in Hawaii and the Western world, some historians have pointed out a side effect which may explain some of Mrs. Takata's choices around Reiki.[62] The many male Japanese immigrants who came to the Hawaiian plantations – like Mrs. Takata's father, who came to Hawaii alone at age 24 – also came to communities which had been cut off from their cultural and religious roots. Weddings and funeral ceremonies, the cycles of the year, all the important religious observances that marked events of their lives, had been part of the Japanese infrastructure left behind when they came to Hawaii.

After a rather unsuccessful attempt by Christian missionaries – and even a few Japanese converts to Christianity – to convert the immigrant population on Hawaii to Christianity, Japanese Buddhists arrived to establish Buddhist centers and revive the religion the vast majority of the immigrants had been raised in. The first Buddhist temple in Hawaii was dedicated in Honolulu in 1900 (it would have been earlier but the formal dedication was delayed by a bubonic plague outbreak).[63] The Y.M.B.A. started concurrently, fostering a sense of community and cohesion through the Japanese-American community, first in Honolulu and then throughout the islands.

In 1918, the same year Saichi brought the Japanese men of the Kealia plantation together for a Y.M.B.A. chapter, the main temple of Hongwanji was completed in Honolulu. The mission's second bishop, the Rev. Yemyo Imamura, wrote a pamphlet explaining the Buddhist mission in Hawaii. Apparently Imamura was clear

"Buddhism must be made palatable for the Island

population. If the immigrant was living on an American island, then his religion also had to reflect the attitudes and cultural tastes of his ambivalent social environment. If his ancient beliefs and practices were blasphemed as pagan and non-American, then efforts had to be made to show the similarities of Buddhism and Christianity."[64]

The design of the temple itself, according to the current Hongwanji Betsuin history, included elements from India, China, Japan and the West:

> "[I]n order to highlight the fact that Japanese immigrants in Hawaii were loyal Americans, and to facilitate the acceptance of Buddhism as an American faith tradition, wooden pews, a high wooden pulpit, pipe organ, hymnals (gatha books) and Sunday services were instituted along with the traditional Japanese gold and brass altar decorations centered around the... image of Amida Buddha."[65]

This strategy, emphasizing the similarities of Buddhism and Christianity, can be seen as a keynote throughout Mrs. Takata's life. She definitely was a Buddhist. She donated generously to the Buddhist temple in Hawaii at least through the 1960's. In fact, she was the first to donate – $500, which was quite a bit in 1961 – towards a new building in honor of the 75th anniversary in Hilo.[66] In her home in Iowa at the very end of her life, she had a shrine carefully hidden from her American neighbors which honored her ancestors and her husband, Saichi.[67] On the other hand, Mrs. Takata generally referred to God from a Christian perspective, worked extensively with ministers, and presented herself and her beliefs in a way which blended in with general American Judeo-Christian culture. The influence of the Y.M.B.A. clarifies some otherwise difficult-to-understand ways she presented herself and Reiki.

5 HAWAYO TO JAPAN

By 1935, Hawayo Takata had become exhausted. She was supporting her two daughters and helping her parents, working for Countess Bonzi, filling in as a clerk at the Kealia Store, serving as a water collector.... As she wrote in 1974, recalling that time, "After my husband's transition, I... worked very hard to become financially able to care for my family. From 1930 to 1935 I had little rest, overworking myself, which finally resulted in a nervous breakdown. In addition, I had severe physical problems, a painful abdominal condition which required surgery, and emphysema, an outgrowth of asthma, which prevented use of the anesthetic."[68] She said, "And the doctor said, 'You need operation, but we cannot perform that because you have no husband, and we do not want your children to be orphans.'"[69]

At just this time, one of Hawayo's sisters died in four days of tetanus. The Kawamura parents had gone to Japan for a year's visit, the first time Otogoro (Hawayo's father) had been back to Japan since he emigrated in 1891. Hawayo decided she needed to give her parents the sad news of her sister's death in person, and get help for her own health issues at the same time. She had also been waiting for five years to take Saichi's ashes to Japan for a second funeral.

On October 8, 1935, Hawayo Takata sailed from Honolulu on the ship *Asama Maru* bound for Yokohama. With her were her younger daughter Alice, age nine; her sister-in-law Katsuyo Takata, age 36; and Hanako and Wilfred Takata, the oldest and youngest of Katsuyo's children (ages seventeen and five respectively).[70] Her sister-in-law had generously offered to accompany her. Hawayo also carried her husband's ashes to give him a second funeral in Kyoto at the Ohtani Temple and Mausoleum.

On the ship, Mrs. Takata met a Buddhist minister from Kona, Hawaii who was going to work at the temple in Kyoto. He offered to help her with Saichi's ashes so she would not need to carry them all over Japan. She entrusted the ashes to him and made a appointment to meet for Saichi's second funeral in six months, on March 26, 1936, when she was sure she would be well enough to be there. Meanwhile, first she traveled to Yamaguchi to tell her parents about her sister Fusae's death.[71]

After a visit with her parents and then traveling together to her mother's mother in Hiroshima, Hawayo left her family to go to Tokyo. She took Alice with her and arranged to meet the rest of the family in Kyoto on March 24.

In Tokyo, Mrs. Takata went to the Maeda Hospital in Akasaka where Saichi had known the head surgeon who founded the hospital seven years earlier. They welcomed her and examined her. However, they insisted she first rest and gain a few pounds before talking about surgery. Dr. Maeda told her, "Do not think of this as a hospital, but a resort hotel. Enjoy your stay."[72] He introduced her to his sister, Mrs. Shimura, who worked there as a dietician.

Mrs. Takata spent three weeks resting, eating and getting stronger. They then did a thorough medical examination, and the doctor told her, "You have a tumor and gall stones and appendicitis. The appendix should come out; and that's why you have your stomach ache all the time. And those are the things that we are going to do and you are now able to go through this operation because your asthma has quieted down." Her surgery was scheduled for seven the next morning.

The next morning, Mrs. Takata had fasted and was prepped for surgery. While she was lying in the operating room,

> "The doctors came in and they were at the sink, and they were washing and scrubbing, sterilizing their hands and I could hear the faucets going on, splashing, and they were talking but I could not understand what they were talking about, but they were having their conversation. I was very, very still, lying on the bed. All of a sudden I heard a voice, and I said, 'My, is anybody around?' and I opened my eyes. I looked all around, up to the ceiling and to the side. I saw the nurse was very busy, going back and forth, back and forth. And I said, 'That's not the nurse's voice.' But this voice said, 'Operation not necessary, operation not necessary.' And then I heard this twice. When I heard it the first time, I said 'I am just nuts. I am crazy. I am hearing things.' But on the second, I began to pinch myself. And I said, 'If I heard, I'm not crazy. And if I hear it the third time I am going to accept... and I heard it louder the third time, and it said, 'Operation not necessary.' So I said, 'I'm not crazy.' but I said, 'What can I do, I am on the operating table?' And the voice said, 'Ask...ask...ask." So I said, 'Ask who, who do I ask?' And the voice came back and said, 'The head surgeon, the head surgeon, the head surgeon.' And the voice went away. And so I slipped off from the bed and stood on the floor."

At this point the nurse was annoyed because Mrs. Takata had ruined all the sterilization and pre-op preparations. However, Mrs. Takata insisted that she wasn't afraid of the surgery but she wanted another option. She said to the doctor, "I am an outsider. But you will know. Is there any kind of a therapy or a treatment that I can try that you think would help me?"

"He thought for a few seconds and said, 'Yes, but it all depends on how much time you have in here in Tokyo.' I asked how long.... He said, 'I don't know. You have to try. But when you try, we shall find out.' Those were the exact words. 'And how much time do you have?' I said, 'How much is it going to take?' He said, 'Well, two months, two weeks, maybe four months, maybe one year. Who knows? You have to try. It all depends on how well you respond.... That is the answer.' Just because he said one year, I doubted him. And I said, 'Doctor, I can stay two years, I have time.' He said, 'Wonderful. If you have two years, wonderful.' He said, 'There are many people who come through here for a cure and a tour of Japan and they do it all in sixty days. Then if you are one of them, you can walk out of the hospital in three weeks. That's plenty of time to get well and strong enough to go around and visit Japan.' I said, 'No, I didn't come here to travel or to see Japan, but for help. Number one, help. And so, if I may start this treatment?'"

At that point, the doctor summoned his sister, Mrs. Shimura, from her work as the dietician in the hospital kitchen. Later Mrs. Takata discovered that Mrs. Shimura had been in a coma dying of dysentery and recovered after this other kind of treatment. Since then, her brother recommended this alternative whenever someone did not want drugs or surgery.

Mrs. Shimura escorted Mrs. Takata to "a studio where they were taking people to give them drugless and bloodless treatments" in the Shinanomachi district of Tokyo. There were eight beds with sixteen practitioners, as well as the "head man, Dr. Hayashi and his wife, Mrs. Hayashi who acted as the 'hostess.'" Mrs. Takata was the last patient of the day and received her first Reiki treatment. She was very curious about what was happening. It was "so sweet and everything sounds so good to my ears" that she kept pinching herself to see whether she was dreaming. When she returned to where she was staying in the hospital, she saw her side was black-and-blue from where she had been pinching herself.

The next morning Mrs. Takata was determined to be first in line at the clinic, except she pointed out the hospital required her to eat breakfast at 7 so she could not leave as early as she would have liked. After the required breakfast, she took a streetcar to the clinic and was number four for the day. She had noticed the hands of the people working on her were warm and seemed to vibrate. When she arrived, she made sure to look around the bed she was assigned to, and she checked the walls and ceiling for wires. Nothing was visible. Then, given her experience the day before, she decided they must have some kind of machines in their kimono sleeves.

While Mrs. Takata was lying on the bed, she suddenly lifted one of the men's kimono sleeves. The man was startled, and then pulled a tissue from his kimono sleeve and offered it to Mrs. Takata, saying "Handkerchief?" She said she did not need a handkerchief,

"'I do not wish to cry. There's nothing to use this handkerchief for. But I am interested in your pocket because I thought you had some kind of an instrument or battery.' And so, I said, 'Where is the machine? Machine, machine.' And he started to laugh. And he flipped his sleeves on his arms, and both sleeves went up, and they were empty. And... he laughed so hard... he almost fell off the stool backwards. And this time, when I saw him, I began to laugh because it was such a funny sight. The master who was attending other patients came very fast, just swishing the tatami mat, and said, 'What is this, the happy laugh?' He said, 'To laugh is just wonderful medicine. Everybody should laugh.' And he said, 'If there is anything that is happy, happy,' he said, 'I would like to laugh with you.' He said, 'Please tell me.'"

The practitioner told him the "lady from Hawaii" thought there was a machine in his sleeve and he thought she wanted a tissue.

Mrs. Takata said to Dr. Hayashi, "I could feel the vibration. They were not ordinary hands... he must have some kind of a connection with some kind of a force or power." As Mrs. Takata told it, Dr. Hayashi's response was,

"'Not any kind of electricity.' He said, 'This is Reiki.' So, I looked straight into his eyes and I said, 'I do not understand, because I'm not too familiar with Japanese.' And he said, 'You are right. Reiki is Japanese word. But I know some English. When I was a cadet, I was on a boat training ship and went to Los Angeles, New York, Hawaii many, many times, San Francisco, went around the world, Australia, all over.... This in English is called "universal life energy"' [said with a] Japanese accent. But then I understood. Then he pointed to space, two hands up, and he said, 'It comes from the sun, from the space, from the moon, or from the space, this is universal.' And he raised his two hands up, and he waved them. And he said, 'The only thing that is different between you and I, we have the contact. You don't, but now, my practitioners all have the contact. They can use it and they are filling your body with life energy. And this is too, too big, we cannot measure it. Too, too deep, deeper than the ocean. We cannot fathom. Therefore in Japanese we call it Reiki.'"

Dr. Hayashi asked Mrs. Takata whether she knew about radio (she comments here while telling the story that in 1935 Hawaii, radio was nothing like radio today), and used another analogy:

"'When the radio station broadcasts, there is no

lines connected from the radio station to your home. But when you turn on the knob and when you contact the station, then, if they were broadcasting sound, you get music. And when they are broadcasting speech, you get speech. And that is radio, you don't know how. Because you are not a radio technician, nor am I. But the principles are the same. It goes through space without a wire. Therefore... you have to accept that this great force can be contacted, and when you have the contact, then it is automatic, universal, and then it is just limitless, unlimited power, when you have the switch on. And when you want to stop, all you have to do is take your hands off.'"

At the end of that day, after all her questions, Dr. Hayashi made a little speech to all his practitioners:

"'Mrs. Takata is an American. She looks Japanese and has a Japanese name but she is an American born in Hawaii, an American citizen. And therefore, what she has just expressed is democracy. That's how all Americans are, very open, very frank. And so, in Hawaii this is nothing strange or not even rude. But in Japan, the ladies are very calmer and they restrain from expressing themselves. And the law of the Japanese philosophy is ladies do not display emotions in public.'"

Mrs. Takata notes the practitioners understood her better and did not "make a big joke of it" after that.

Later, Mrs. Shimura told Mrs. Takata if she had questions to come to her. She shared her own experience being brought out of a coma by a Reiki practitioner. She told Mrs. Takata, "I took training when I was able, when I got strong enough I took training. Here [in the hospital], I have been helping people... even in the food. I touch all the food and all the salads, and the tofu... I vitalize it and everything I touch is vitalized."

Mrs. Takata became very interested and asked how she

could also be trained. However, Mrs. Shimura told her,
  "'Ah, that is another story. We have given many,
  many cultures to the outside world. We have given
  Kendo, Judo, Karate, tea arrangements, flower
  arrangement. These are all cultures. But Reiki, no,
  we guard it with a fence around it. It shall not get
  out of Japan.'"
As she told it, Mrs. Takata then told Mrs. Shimura,
  "'I have found my life. How can I go home without
  it?... I was drawn here for some good purpose. But, I
  said, if that is the rule and the law of Reiki, well, I'm
  not going to say any more. But I am going to find a
  way.'"
After three weeks, during which she was still staying at
the Maeda Hospital and going to the Reiki clinic for
treatments on a daily basis, she saw Dr. Maeda in the hall.
He asked how she was doing. Mrs. Takata said,
  "Here was my opportunity, it took courage, but I
  said, 'Doctor, there is one thing. I have to ask a
  great, great favor of you.' He said, 'What is it?' I said,
  'Only you can help me.' He said, 'Is that so? What is
  it?' I said, 'Doctor, I came here for some good
  reason and now I am taking these treatments, I am
  getting well. I want to learn. I don't want to go
  home empty-handed. Please, Doctor, help me.' He
  said, 'Ah, that is another story.' I said, 'Why?' He
  said, 'Because they have etiquette, they have rules
  and I think this association does not want to accept
  outsiders.'"
Mrs. Takata convinced him, telling him he was a "great
humanitarian," and that if he wrote a letter to Dr. Hayashi
explaining she lived very far away and needed to learn Reiki
just for herself and her family, he would be saving an entire
family:
  "'Please tell Dr. Hayashi that Takata came here to
  get well and she is seeking for health. But she
  cannot come to Japan every time she needs a

treatment. That's too far and too costly. She can't do it. So while she is here, she wants to learn Reiki and she will help herself and her family. That is all she wants to do, is help herself and her family, so that she can stand on her feet and she can support the family and help the family so that the family can live a little longer. They are losing children when they are twenty years old, eighteen years old, you know, and twenty-five years old. And that is too, too sad a life, too sad. And I am only thirty-five. I am only thirty-five and I don't want to die.'"

Dr. Maeda saw she was sincere. Then he asked her how she was going to pay for this.

"He said, 'Are you willing to pay the price?' And he poked a finger almost in my eye. And I said, 'Doctor, if I can buy my life, why not? Without life I am nobody. I'm nothing. If I can, I shall.' And he said, 'You got that money here?' I said, 'I don't know, I don't know how much.' He said, 'I don't know, too. I don't know. But you're the first outsider.'... I said, 'I've got a house. I've got a house.' 'Alright, what you going to do? Are you going to sell it? Then you won't have a roof over your head.' I said, 'Don't worry about that. When I come to that point, I'm going to do the worrying. I don't let you worry about that.... I am only thirty-five, and when I am fifty ... I might have two houses. What is one house if I die? Nothing.'"

After that, Dr. Maeda went to his office and wrote a letter to Dr. Hayashi. Mrs. Takata made a point of the fact that the letter was not typewritten by his secretary, but written with a brush on a scroll in the traditional style. The scroll was almost three yards long. Apparently the letter asked Dr. Hayashi to teach Mrs. Takata "on a humanitarian basis" since she could not come back to Japan every time she or her family needed Reiki. According to Mrs. Takata, Dr. Hayashi was very impressed by this personal letter from such a famous person. He met with the Board of Directors, and they decided to make her a special "Honorary Member." Because it was "special," they could teach her.

Dr. Hayashi taught classes for beginners once a month. Mrs. Takata joined the next class and learned what she later called the First Degree. Dr. Hayashi "initiated" her "to make the contact with this limitless power." Without going into detail, she said this contact would be "made in four small steps." Today we know there are four energy activations, or Attunements, in the First Degree of the intact science of Real Reiki®. Without every one of those four activations in order – four steps – the student does not have the full capacity for the First Degree. Mrs. Takata's first certificate in a rough translation reads:

> "Hiromi Takata [*Ed.: Hiromi was her middle, more Japanese name*] is hereby conferred the secret principles of the Usui Reiki Ryoho [the Usui method of Reiki]. Dated this 13th day of December, 1935.
>
> Chujiro Hayashi
> Reijusha"[73]

Mrs. Takata herself was feeling much better after three weeks of daily hands-on sessions. She continued, receiving hands-on daily for four months, and then was finally feeling completely well. At this point, it was also time to meet the rest of her family in Kyoto for Saichi's funeral.

After the funeral ceremonies, her parents returned with her to Tokyo where they lived in a small cottage. Mrs. Takata began to feel she should actually practice using Reiki, so she sent her parents, daughter Alice, and her sister-in-law and family back to Hawaii. They left on April 11, 1936 on the *Empress of Canada.*[74] Mrs. Takata saw them off at the pier and then moved into Dr. Hayashi's house, where she lived with his family for the next two months.

In the mornings Mrs. Takata received hands-on or acted as a practitioner in Dr. Hayashi's clinic. They all ate lunch from twelve to one. Then Dr. Hayashi sent his students out to clients' houses, one each afternoon. Mrs. Takata would get on the train, sometimes for an hour or two, and find a house where she would do a Reiki session. When she returned, the Hayashis would have dinner waiting for her. Only later did she find out she was being tested, and the clients were reporting back to Dr. Hayashi when Mrs. Takata arrived, what she did, and how long she was there. She did exactly as she was told, showing she was very serious about the work and could be trusted to do what she promised.

On June 2, 1936, knowing she had to return to her family and jobs, Hawayo Takata sailed on the *Taiyo Maru* back to Honolulu, arriving in Hawaii on June 10. Dr. Hayashi later issued another certificate for the additional study Mrs. Takata had completed up until that point, including what we now can see was being able to attune others at least to The First Degree:

"Hawayo Takado

Having been conferred the secret principles of the spiritual healing method on December 10, 1935, the above-named individual returned and stayed at this institute until May 8, 1936, and engaged in the studies of treatment of various illnesses directly under my supervision and instruction and, although her stay with the institute was not long, her gifted talent, enthusiasm and sincerity made possible quick diagnoses and effective treatment and her spiritual empowerment has successfully treated various illness, and being acknowledged to be the most appropriate to teach the Method to others, she has received the method of relaying to others the mystic/miraculous medium/power for the spiritual healing method.

Dated this 1st day of October, 1936.
    Chujiro Hayashi
    President, Hayashi Reiki Study Institute"[75]

This is one of the few early clues to the different levels of training. After her further study, Mrs. Takata "has received the method of relaying to others the mystic/miraculous medium/power for the... method," which rewritten in modern English states she was now capable of giving others the power to use Reiki for themselves, what we now call the Third Degree of Real Reiki®.

6 A Reiki Master in Hawaii

Upon her return from Japan in 1936, Mrs. Takata continued what she called "supervising the estate." By this time, she had much more responsibility over those in the Bonzi household. As she worked with the residents, when she saw an illness or problem, she offered to do something that might help. The first person was the cook's daughter who had had three operations for some sort of infection. There was still a large abscess along with a terrible incision. Mrs. Takata said, "I am not going to hurt you because the treatments are very gentle. And all I am going to do is lay my hand and just touch you. That is all. There shall be no pain, nothing to be afraid." The little girl's incision began to drain, and over a period of days, she was healed. One of the "yard boys" was recovering from an appendectomy. Mrs. Takata applied Reiki and he recovered and left the hospital.[76]

Stories started to spread that she had brought something special back from Japan. One morning Mrs. Takata woke up to find ten people milling around in front of the house arguing about who would get to see her first. With the help and advice of the postmaster, who seems to have served as the local authority, she decided to open an office. The word went out to wait until it was announced in the newspaper

53

and then everyone would be able to experience Reiki.

On October 6, 1936, Mrs. Takata opened an office in Ota Cottage on Hauala Street in Kapaa, Kauai. She called herself a "practitioner" and advertised "Reiki Sanitarium Treatments, Absolutely Drugless." The office was open from 4 to 8 each afternoon, with special free clinics for children under six months every Saturday. She also mentioned "Special treatments for stomach and internal ailments; nervous diseases and general debility."[77]

The word "sanitarium" (as different from the European "sanatorium") became the American spelling after the famous John Harvey Kellogg of Kellogg Cereals founded his health center in 1866 in Battle Creek, Michigan. By the early 1900's, "Battle Creek Sanitarium was world renowned and became the 'in' place for the rich and famous to seek their lost health, to listen to health lectures and to learn and practice the principles of a healthy lifestyle."[78] A sanitarium became the word for an upscale health resort. This American meaning matches Mrs. Takata's aspirations for her health-restoring practice. There were also a few other places in the islands which used the word "sanitarium," so Mrs. Takata was advertising something which newspaper readers would find familiar.

The following year, Mrs. Takata returned to Japan for more training and to consult with Dr. Hayashi about some experiences she had been having. She sailed again on the *Taiyo Maru*, leaving Honolulu on June 29, 1937. Again she stayed with the Hayashi family, and practiced using Reiki every day. "I was working at his studio, and I had many, many treatments and I gave treatments and I worked very hard. And he was very impressed."

Dr. Hayashi's daughter, Kiyoe, had become engaged to be married the following April. Mrs. Takata said,

> "'Please, Miss Hayashi, will you come home with me and visit Hawaii? Because once you are married you shall be a housewife, a very obedient housewife and there shall be no trips outside of this country unless

your husband will take you. Meanwhile, while you are single, why not visit Hawaii?"[79]

After some discussion, Mrs. Hayashi encouraged her husband to chaperone their daughter to Hawaii, and Dr. Hayashi would spend months "visiting and helping establish Reiki in Hawaii."[80]

Mrs. Takata's account places more emphasis on Kiyoe's personal visit rather than Dr. Hayashi going to Hawaii to train her further. However, although there is no written documentation confirming this speculation, remember that Dr. Hayashi had been a naval officer. Looking at the circumstances, it is very likely he was aware the Japanese would soon be at war. Everyone who studied Reiki with him was male. They were all of a certain class and education. There was no guarantee any of the students he knew in Japan would live through a war. After Mrs. Takata's commitment and dedication to learning Reiki, and after getting to know her when she lived in Dr. Hayashi's house, he would have known well that she could be a trustworthy and protective guardian of the secrets of Reiki. Even though Mrs. Takata did not really talk about Dr. Hayashi's choice to give her the Keys to Reiki, the situation and timing offer some plausible clues into his possible reasons for that decision.

Mrs. Takata sailed for Hawaii on September 15, 1937, and Dr. Chujiro Hayashi and Miss Kiyoe Hayashi sailed the following week, on September 24. On the immigration documents, Dr. Hayashi listed his occupation as "Master of Hayashi Reiki Kenkyu Japanese"; someone wrote in script under that typewritten title "Spiritual Healer."[81] The Hayashis arrived in Honolulu on October 2, 1937.

Mrs. Takata rented space in Honolulu and Dr. Hayashi gave many lectures and taught classes over the following months. The Japanese-language newspaper, the *Hawaii Hochi*, covered the months of his visit with extensive articles and photographs. There was a complicated, lengthy and intense legal complaint instigated and pursued by a "disgruntled person." After numerous interviews with the police and investigation by immigration authorities, Mrs. Takata and Dr. Hayashi proved he was not taking massive amounts of money from people in Hawaii. In fact, he had brought with him a large sum of money in travelers checks with the Japanese Imperial stamp on each one. In the end, all charges were dropped, but it was a major issue throughout his visit.

Dr. Chujiro Hayashi in Hawaii (1937-38)

The Hayashis were scheduled to depart Honolulu on February 22. On February 21, there was a gala banquet – all the women in kimono, the men in business suits – to honor Dr. Hayashi and thank him for everything he had done and all the new Reiki students he had taught. On that day, Dr. Hayashi announced Mrs. Takata was now a Reiki Master and was appointed to carry on the work started in Hawaii. He gave her one more certificate, witnessed, notarized and in English:

THIS IS TO CERTIFY that Mrs. Hawayo Takata, an American citizen born in the Territory of Hawaii, after a course of study and training in the Usui system of Reiki healing undertaken under my personal supervision during a visit to Japan in 1935 and subsequently, has passed all the tests and proved worthy and capable of administering the treatment and of conferring the power of Reiki on others.

THEREFORE I, Dr. Chujiro Hayashi, by virtue of my authority as a Master of the Usui Reiki system of drugless healing, do hereby confer upon Mrs. Hawayo Takata the full power and authority to practice the Reiki system and to impart to others the secret knowledge and the gift of healing under this system.

MRS HAWAYO TAKATA is hereby certified by me as a practitioner and Master of Dr. Usui's Reiki system of healing, at this time the only person in the United States authorized to confer similar powers on others and one of the thirteen fully qualified as a Master of the profession.

Signed by me this 21st day of February, 1938, in the city and county of Honolulu, territory of Hawaii.

(SIGNED) [Chujiro Hayashi][82]

On February 22, 1938, the Hayashis sailed for Japan. Hawayo Takata had been named Reiki Master for Hawaii and the United States.

After all the legal problems with the "disgruntled person" while Dr. Hayashi was visiting, Mrs. Takata knew a number of legal authorities. One day, after Dr. Hayashi was

"far away in the mid-ocean, the police came one day unexpected. He said, 'Takata, you had a rough time, didn't you?' I said, 'Yes, because I was a country jack, and I didn't know. But then you see, I am always in the right, because when I came to Honolulu, country jack as I was, I got a license.' And then, I said, 'Who gave me the license? Mr. Wilfred Tsukiyama, the attorney general [*Ed.: actually City Attorney for Honolulu, the second Japanese-American ever to be admitted to the bar.*[83]] I went to him, a Japanese and a very, very good attorney.... So I went to him and said, 'I am from the country and I don't know a thing about law, but I am going to practice in Honolulu and I need to have some kind of a license.' He said, 'I am glad you came to me, you need a license.' And so he gave it to me and he said, 'Frame it and put it in the room where anybody can see.' So I did."[84]

The license Mrs. Takata got was a "massage license," that being the closest existing category to the hands-on she was offering. However, in interviews she always emphasized there is "no manipulation," making it clear this was not massage. It was, however, another piece to some of the confusion around Reiki being a kind of massage or bodywork.

The following year is somewhat obscure. According to her own account, the new "Archbishop" of the local Jodo Mission, who after long-term laryngitis had regained his voice under Dr. Hayashi's care, decided to travel to California to visit Buddhist temples and meet the clergy there. He was planning to take twelve others with him, but none of them spoke English. He invited Mrs. Takata to travel with them to be their interpreter. Meanwhile, the managing editor of the newspaper (presumably the *Hawaii Hochi*, since he knew her well by then) was encouraging Mrs. Takata to sue the person who had caused so much trouble when Dr. Hayashi was there. She insisted that she lived a peaceful life. Instead, she wanted to better herself and "polish" her skills.

At this point, Mrs. Takata says she went to the West Coast with the Buddhist Archbishop and his entourage. She spent some weeks translating menus in the restaurants and enjoying a vacation with the group. She had applied to the National College of Drugless Physicians (now the National University of Health Sciences) in Chicago and been accepted. At the end of this "vacation" with the Buddhists, she took a train to Chicago to attend the college. She says she studied Swedish massage, colonics and anatomy. She also received a complete physical exam which showed there was only a small area of scar tissue "as big as a dime"[85] where she had had a tumor prior to going to Japan. Otherwise she was in excellent physical condition.

While in the Chicago area, Mrs. Takata also visited Veronica Flaherty, a woman she had met on the ship to Japan the previous year. Miss Flaherty was a librarian at the Horace Mann High School in Chicago and lived in Gary, Indiana. A newspaper clipping about a reception held in Mrs. Takata's honor shows Mrs. Takata formally dressed in her kimono, and Miss Flaherty's young niece also dressed in Japanese garb, a striking image given the anti-Japanese sentiment which would seize the country only a few years later.[86]

In May 1939, Mrs. Takata returned to Hawaii and announced the opening of a "branch" office in Hilo. The "Big Island" obviously had a lot more people and potential than Kauai. She now had an assistant, Dr. Ruth Hart of Chicago, who was a chiropractor. The National College for Drugless Physicians trained chiropractors, so it is not unlikely to think she met Dr. Hart while in Chicago and convinced her to come practice for a while in the exotic Territory of Hawaii. The office hours were quite expanded from Mrs. Takata's initial opening two years before: 8 a.m. to 4:30 p.m. with evenings by appointment. The article quotes Mrs. Takata as remarking, "I do not give any medicine or herbs, nor do I go in for regular massaging. My method is entirely scientific, and not religious at all. My patients do not have to believe in me or even concentrate while I am working on them."[87]

After her study in Chicago, though, Mrs. Takata seems to have decided to advertise Reiki as a kind of massage, even as she said Reiki did not involve massaging. The term "massage" was probably much more understandable and more likely to attract clients... and again, it led to confusion in later years. While Mrs. Takata now had some kind of massage training, Real Reiki® itself was not and is not a kind of massage. Students do not need to study massage to use it for themselves. The technique itself is not a bodywork method, although one form of applying the energy involves the hands.

The local newspapers now listed Mrs. Takata as a "Reiki massage expert"[88] and reported her students had completed courses in "Reiki massage treatments."[89] By the end of August, Mrs. Takata had expanded into larger quarters in Hilo and added two practitioners, Miss Yoshiko Hirata and Miss Emma Martin, who was the daughter of Sheriff Henry Martin.[90] By November 1939, Mrs. Takata's newspaper notice read, "Reiki health restoring, rejuvenating nerve and glandular treatments. Swedish massage for reducing and good circulation. All manipulations by hand."[91]

At home, Mrs. Takata's elder daughter, nineteen-year-old Julia, traveled to Japan in August 1939 for a year's study, while fourteen-year-old Alice returned to Kauai to stay with her grandparents during the school year. Mrs. Takata continued to work in Hilo, which is approximately 320 miles from the island of Kauai.[92]

In 1939, the first of Mrs. Takata's long-term business ventures showed up in print: she obtained four lots of land in Waikiki.[93] Beginning now and until the end of her life, Mrs. Takata made smart investments and built an income based upon property and rents, never relying upon income from her work with Reiki.

This was a time when many Japanese-Americans were putting down roots, buying property and expanding their financial bases out of their initial role as immigrant hired help. In 1901, the labor on sugar plantations was 70%

Japanese; by 1935, only 25% of those working on the plantations were of Japanese ancestry. By the mid-1930's, "the interest among the Japanese to invest their savings in real estate has been quite keen."[94] The author, writing in 1938, attributed this to the majority of Japanese choosing to make Hawaii their permanent residence.

Dr. Chujiro Hayashi died in 1940, approximately 61 years old. Passenger manifests show Mrs. Takata returned to Japan in March 1940 for two months. According to her immigration declaration on her return, she had been visiting "T. Hayashi," not "C. Hayashi," so she may have traveled back for the funeral services and to be with the family.[95] Other than saying Dr. Hayashi died in 1940, she revealed nothing about that trip and did not mention it in her autobiography.

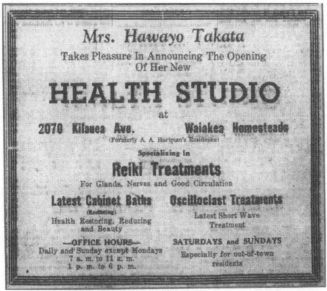

Newspaper Ad for Mrs. Takata's Health Studio (1940)

Upon her return from Japan, Mrs. Takata really built up her practice in Hilo. After a visit to two schoolteachers she had met, she opened a new Health Studio in what had been a private home in the Waiakea Homesteads area. This is probably when she moved her parents and Alice from Kauai to Hilo to live with her. The display ad for her studio emphasizes the latest treatments and facilities.[96]

She went to mahjongg parties, took her mother out to a "chop sui dinner,"[97] and gave parties in honor of friends visiting Hawaii. Everything was in place for her to develop her Reiki business and live a successful and fulfilling life.

7 WAR AND THE JAPANESE

In 1941, Hawayo Takata had her studio in Hilo, on the island of Hawai'i. Honolulu, on the island of Oahu, is approximately 210 miles northwest of Hilo, past the islands of Maui and Molokai. The island of Kauai is another 110 miles northwest of Honolulu.

At 7:55 a.m. on Sunday morning, December 7, 1941, just as the military's duty shifts changed, a fleet of Japanese bombers attacked the naval base at Pearl Harbor near Honolulu and decimated the U.S. ships and planes stationed on Oahu.[98] By mid-afternoon, the Territory of Hawaii was under martial law. Unlike anything imposed on U.S. soil before or since, Hawaii became both under martial law and run by a military government. Civil courts were suspended, radio stations controlled by the authorities, and all foreign-language schools and newspapers closed.[99]

Unlike on the mainland, few Hawaiian Japanese were interned during World War II. Japanese comprised 38% of the islands' population and 31% of registered voters.[100] The economy would have ground to a halt without the residents of Japanese ancestry. However, anyone of Japanese ancestry was not permitted to serve in the military until 1943. A strong prejudice against the Japanese, even in Hawaii, where whites were much more accustomed to their Japanese neighbors than on the mainland, superseded the pre-war harmony.

Mrs. Takata said little about the Pearl Harbor attack or the war in general. On December 7, she was working in Hilo. Everyone heard about the attack on the radio. A woman whom she had taught lived in Honolulu, and her son volunteered to help clean up after the attack. What he saw so horrified him that when he went home that night, he was in shock and all his hair had fallen out. The woman frantically called Mrs. Takata for help, and Mrs. Takata promised to be there as soon as possible. She did in fact go to Honolulu soon after and use Reiki with the young man. He recovered and all his hair grew back in, although there were white patches in it.[101]

Immediately after Pearl Harbor, families were encouraged to evacuate to the West Coast. At the same time, many soldiers and auxiliary forces were transported to the islands. Suddenly the population exploded, leading to housing and food shortages. As Mrs. Takata recounts,

"When the war broke out in 1941, and in 1942, when the army started to move in, all these farmers, they were expert in Reiki already. And all the farmers became very, very wealthy, because the government said, 'We're going to have 50,000 soldiers in this area and we want food. We want you to grow lettuce, celery, cabbage, carrots, everything what the farm grows we will buy on a very, very, very big scale.' ... The farmers said, 'We have Reiki and we're healthy. We can put in our best.' And they treated the seeds [with Reiki] before they were planted. And they had beautiful crops. And every farmer was a success and every space was planted. And therefore the farmers were a great, great success."[102]

Mrs. Takata had had many students on a number of ranches before the war. She often told stories of what the ranchers had taught her about using Reiki with their livestock:

"During this period the cowboys experienced that they could handle the cattle. And when they knew when there was going to be a newborn baby, they would corral the cow into a shed, and that night they would watch and take care of the newborn by wrapping them up in a warm blanket and vitalizing the newborn with Reiki.... They said, 'We have not lost one newborn.' This is a great credit to Reiki.... 'Also, we have experience on poorer cows that were not as productive. We worked on them [longer] ...and then they also became productive.' And this experience, although I am a Reiki Master, I did not have in person, but I was very happy to know because Reiki works on everything that has life, including animals."[103]

Some of the farmers also reported using Reiki with their chickens, holding the eggs and the newborn chicks. Another farmer had honeybees and invited Mrs. Takata to visit and see how his bees were thriving after he learned Reiki from her. In her five years of practice before the war, Mrs. Takata had taught a lot of people. The ranches and plantations on several islands had their Reiki practitioners, and it seems to have made a distinct difference in the stresses of wartime. Mrs. Takata's summation was:

"...when the war came, all the farmers became very, very wealthy.... Even overgrown cabbages were sold. They didn't have to be...normal size or uniform size, every stalk of celery, every root of carrots and turnips and beans, all were sold and picked up by the army. And when they had many, many marines there, they had about 50,000 people. So this was a great experience."[104]

During the war, Mrs. Takata continued offering Reiki at her studio in Hilo. Her twenty-one-year-old daughter, Julia, moved to Honolulu for the second half of 1942. Kay Kurata, who worked for the Corps of Engineers, moved from

Honolulu to Hilo to live with Mrs. Takata in October 1942[105] and became a lifelong family friend. In September 1944, Hawayo Takata's mother Hatsu died. She probably was about eighty. Mrs. Takata placed an ad of thanks in the newspaper on behalf of the family.[106]

The Takata family continued to be very connected and close to each other. Katsuyo Takata had also become a widow when her husband, Saichi's brother Kenichi, died in 1938 at the age of forty-five. Henry Takata, Katsuyo's son and Mrs. Takata's nephew, visited her in Hilo in 1945 after he graduated from high school on Kauai. Katsuyo and Hawayo were the same age, and Katsuyo's youngest, Wilfred, was still only in his early teens during the war. Hawayo owned a house and had a thriving business which seems to have been a great and tangible support to her entire extended family.

Unbelievable in retrospect, martial law continued in Hawaii until late October 1944, despite the outstanding cooperation and willingness shown by the Americans of Japanese descent living in Hawaii.[107] The remnants of military governance lingered in the bureaucracy through at least the next year. The after-effects of war continued to resonate throughout the islands and the Japanese-American community.

The war had a profound effect on Mrs. Takata. Intense awareness and underlying discomfort about race and ethnic differences runs through Mrs. Takata's correspondence. Many years later, Mrs. Takata told Dr. Barbara Ray that she, Dr. Ray, could do a better job of bringing Reiki to the West because her eyes were not "like this"... and she pointed to her slanted Japanese eyes.

8 TAKATA AFTER THE WAR

Before the war, Mrs. Takata had purchased four lots of land in Honolulu. After the war, Hawaii, and especially Honolulu, faced an enormous housing crunch. Mrs. Takata hired a contractor to build apartments on her Waikiki land. On November 6, 1946, the petitions were filed with the Rent Control Commission under the Federal Housing Administration reconversion housing program.[108]

The apartments were nicely appointed, recording that they included shower doors, a mirror in the living room, furnishings including blinds, drapes, soap dish and towel bars, mattress, card table, lamp and built-in ironing board, along with a "smoke stand" and a telephone connection.[109] Notice of completion was published on December 11, 1946.[110] Each apartment was allotted a rent of approximately $82 ($1077 in adjusted 2019 dollars, not taking location into account[111]).

Housing in Hawaii after the war was extremely limited. The influx of military and the associated civilian contractors had flooded the islands during the war. Available housing has been swallowed up by all the additional personnel for the massive war effort. When the war was over, the families who had evacuated to the mainland also returned.

In 1946, the Hawaii Visitors Bureau began a "stay away

for a while" tourism campaign. They wanted to restore the tourism business, which had brought $20 million a year before the war. However, facilities were not quite ready to receive them. The rush was on to refurbish hotels that had been used as military housing and solidify the availability of restaurants, which had been few and far between before the war. As a reporter said in a laudatory *New York Times* article, "These are as lovely islands as there are in the world. Almost four years of war could not scar them permanently."[112] With the increase in airline traffic, Hawaii was also only nine to twelve hours away by plane, compared to five days by ship.

On Kauai, Colonel Spalding's grand Valley House was being converted to a hotel. When the estate was up for sale in 2013, it still had "hand-shaped Roman paving blocks from Italy in the 1800s," two waterfalls, and the oldest lychee grove in Hawaii.[113] The Army had commandeered this property, too. After their changes to the property, Julia Spalding Senni (Countess Bonzi's older sister) put the house on the market on behalf of the family.[114] Mrs. Takata's work for the countess had ended. The countess herself died three years later in California, and her sister Julia died only ten weeks after her.[115]

Immediately after the war ended, Takata's daughter Alice had married a young Japanese-American Army veteran named Kiyoshi Furumoto. The couple moved to Dallas, Texas for him to study medicine. In 1948, the Furumotos had their first child, a daughter they named Phyllis. They almost named her Dallas, the way Alice's mother Hawayo had been named after Hawaii, but they changed their minds.[116] Dr. Furumoto had spent three years at the University of Iowa, so after receiving his medical degree, he went into practice with a friend, Dr. James T. Worrell, in the small town of Keosauqua, Iowa. The Furumotos became the only Japanese living in the town of approximately 1200 residents. In 1958, Alice finally had the time to visit her family in Hawaii after seven years without returning "home," as the Hawaiian papers put it. In the meantime, Mrs. Takata had visited Iowa and her granddaughter Phyllis several times.

In her autobiography, Mrs. Takata also tells a story about her daughter starting the paperwork to adopt a child because she had tried unsuccessfully for nine years to get pregnant. Alice joined her mother in Hawaii, received Reiki treatments, and ate the foods her mother told her to. As Mrs. Takata tells it, less than a year later, she had a grandson. She called both her grandsons "Reiki babies."[117]

Mrs. Takata continued her involvement in different kinds of businesses in Hawaii. According to newspaper notices, she went into partnership with Sophie Bergau in the B & T Health Foods Store, which was renamed "Honolulu House of Health" in February 1947.[118] In her autobiography, she wrote she wanted to invest to help provide an abundance of fresh vegetables and good water which were good for people. However, she could not succeed "due to the negative thinking of my partners."[119] By December, Mrs. Takata dissolved the partnership and sold her interest to Mrs. Bergau; it became the "Sophie Bergau Health Food Store."[120]

Mrs. Takata had good practical reasons to let go of some of her jobs, too. By September 1947, she was an active member of the Hawaiian Hotel Association. The Waimea Ranch Hotel, one of those Hawaiian hotels gearing up for the tourists, hired Mrs. Takata as the hotel manager. The hotel was on the Big Island, up the road from Hilo. Mrs. Takata was one of the group of "hotel men" who met on Maui for a planning and marketing gathering to sell Hawaiian hotels to U.S. travel agents.[121] When the hotel incorporated in October, Mrs. Takata was vice-president of the corporation.[122]

The businesses on the islands actively pursued the tourist trade. 1947 marked the first "Aloha Week" in Hawaii. In November 1948 the Hawaii Visitors Bureau expanded the welcome, with a seven-day festival and inauguration of the "Operation Aloha" and "Operation Orchid" programs.[123] Operation Aloha made sure hula dancers, singers and flowers were present to welcome arriving air passengers. Operation Orchid provided flowers to all ship passengers. Hawaiian businesses were presenting the ideal tropical fantasy vacation at a time when tourists were recovering from wartime austerity.

Aloha Week Hula Dancers (c. 1948-1955)

For the next decade Mrs. Takata kept busy between her duties with the Waimea Ranch Hotel and offering Reiki. After the war she did very little advertising or publicity. For the most part she taught people who found her through word of mouth – a large proportion of whom of course were Japanese – with an occasional trip to the mainland. Around 1948, she began a draft of a book called "The Art of Healing," mostly consisting of experiences of people she had worked on with Reiki.[124] Only five typewritten pages remain, and she never continued with that book.

Mrs. Takata's name appears more often in the newspapers

of the 1950's and 1960's as a winner of golf tournaments than for anything else. However, in 1957 the newspaper did advertise a lecture for the Honolulu Lions Club by Mrs. Hawayo Hiromi Takata simply called "Cosmic Energy."[125]

In 1955 she made an abortive attempt to establish a health spa in La Quinta, California, near Palm Springs. Interestingly enough, La Quinta is considered one of the leading golf destinations in the world. When she mentions the spa, she does not say whether golf was a deciding factor when she chose the location. In a 1974 interview, she said it was "a beautiful place except that the swimming pools I had built for therapeutic water treatments and recreational swimming completely filled up with desert sand during sand storms. My maintenance man did not appreciate this nor did I."[126] In her autobiography, she also says that episode really showed her she was happy 365 days a year in Hawaii.

Hawaii at last became a state on August 21, 1959. Mrs. Takata had always seen herself as an American. She kept the first-day postage stamp issue celebrating Hawaii's becoming the fiftieth state for the rest of her life.

In these decades, Mrs. Takata had contacts with a number of famous people, some of whom were Hollywood stars. She kept these connections extremely quiet, respecting their privacy, and for the most part did not name names. Speculating, it is quite possible that while she was the manager of the Waimea Ranch Hotel, she met a number of famous people and that word got around about Reiki. What can be established – and what she did say in later years – is that she worked for Doris Duke for a number of years.

Doris Duke was an American billionaire heiress who fell in love with Hawaii from her first visit in 1935. She built an extravagant Eastern-inspired house in Honolulu first called "Hale Kapu" (Forbidden House in Hawaiian or else possibly inspired by the Persian home of Ali Kapu in Isfahan[127]) and then renamed Shangri-la after the mythical kingdom in her favorite movie, *Lost Horizon*. The house was not used by the military in World War II because it was too expensive to maintain.[128] It is now a museum of Islamic art.[129] Doris Duke herself became one of the best female surfers in Hawaii and later one of the first women to fly in one of the huge Clipper airplanes from California to Hawaii.[130]

Pan American Airlines "California Clipper" (1939)

Mrs. Takata definitely taught Reiki to Doris Duke. Duke wrote her a letter in 1952 which mentions that she (Duke) was planning to take her "second degree, as you call it."[131]

Doris Duke often used false names while traveling. Only one piece of external evidence shows Duke and Hawayo Takata on the same plane, on February 25, 1957 from Hong Kong to Honolulu.[132] There may well be a number of other trips taken under other names. Some rumors also pair Mrs. Takata with Barbara Hutton, who was the other prominent heiress of the period and often characterized as Duke's rival. However, there is no evidence one way or another: that may have been someone's confusion between the two heiresses who were often linked in the press of the time.

One letter to Mrs. Takata has survived from 1961 which also seems to indicate a fairly regular contact with Hollywood celebrities. The signature is illegible, but the letter begins

"I have wanted to write you many times and tell you that on my return to Hollywood, as I promised you, I spoke to Elizabeth Taylor's husband several times. He wanted to send for you at once, but for some reason or other – probably because she has been ill for so long – Miss Taylor said she just didn't want anybody to do anything to her at all. I hope that some day she'll change her mind."[133]

Miss Taylor's husband at the time would have been Eddie Fisher. The letter also mentions the writer has referred the Feature Editor of Vogue Magazine, Allene Talmey, to Mrs. Takata.

According to tax records, the vast majority of Mrs. Takata's income continued to come from rents of the apartments she owned. She still paid for her "massage license" ($10 in 1962).[134] However, in the first quarter of 1960, Mrs. Takata made $9,350 in rent and $662 from "service business" (listed in her draft calculations as being from "massage").[135] In keeping with a tourist economy dependent upon winter visitors, the "service business" income dropped to $177 in the fourth quarter, and the rents dropped to $5975.

Through the 1960's Mrs. Takata made real estate deals, supported at least one local hopeful politician, donated to the Buddhist temple and other worthy causes, and played a lot of golf. For example, in 1967 "Hawayo Takata captured the 'better none' tournament for women at the Ala Wai course yesterday with a 38½ net."[136] She had moved into a condo, still in the same Waikiki district of Honolulu she had lived in for decades. She was then in her sixties.

9 PUBLICITY

In December 1970, Mrs. Takata turned seventy. After decades of keeping a fairly low profile, over the next couple of years she seemed to increase her public outreach. She gave extended interviews to newspapers when she visited various areas to teach and offer Reiki, and even sat for a TV interview in 1974. She also attended spiritual and healing conferences. It was at one of these conferences that she met Sally Hammond.

Sally Hammond was a reporter with the *New York Post* who, in the early 1970's, took time off her usual job to explore the world of healers. Hammond had been writing for the *Post* since 1957, and in 1966 won a first prize Byline Award in a competition sponsored by the New York Newspaper Reporters Association.

By 1973, there had been an enormous increase of attention around the area known as spiritual healing or psychic healing. The expansive Sixties had opened many people's minds to concepts of something beyond the physical, normal, everyday world. Suddenly even the people who had already been practicing various kinds of esoteric techniques had a much wider audience. One aspect of these techniques included healing of all types. After researching extensively in the United States and Europe, Hammond wrote *We Are All Healers,* one of the early influential overviews of the field of alternative healing.

While researching at one of the healing conventions, Hammond met Hawayo Takata. She devoted four pages of her book to Takata and her healing method, called *reiki.* Hammond described a "crackling bundle of energy in the seat beside me – a small, black-haired woman who appeared to be Japanese.... Her name was Hawayo Hiromi Takata, and she wore fire-engine red slacks, a tunic splashed with tropical flowers and her hair very short and straight."[137]

According to what Hammond wrote, Mrs. Takata said she was going to reveal the secrets of Reiki in 1973 (which we know now did not happen).[138] The interesting aspect to this is Takata made a point of saying there were "secrets" to reveal. Not since before World War II had Mrs. Takata hinted there was more to what she knew.

Later, after her death, a number of Mrs. Takata's students claimed there were no other degrees or parts of the system because Mrs. Takata had never told them anything about them. However, this is commensurate with the decades of silence and secrecy Mrs. Takata had maintained. It is more remarkable that she told Sally Hammond there were any secrets to reveal. And yet, given the context of meeting at a healing convention and Hammond's familiarity with the field, perhaps it is not that surprising.

In the early 1970's Mrs. Takata was also quite active in professional circles. She was a charter member of the Honolulu Chapter of the American Business Women's Association and a member of its Ways and Means Committee. In the January 1974 member directory, however, she chose to be listed as "Self-employed (retired)."[139]

Even though she called herself "retired," the publication of Hammond's *We Are All Healers* sparked a flood of letters to Mrs. Takata. Some were addressed only to "Hawayo Takata, Honolulu, Hawaii;" the post office still managed to deliver them. Mrs. Takata seems to have worked hard to respond to many requests, flying to a number of cities around the United States to teach and to offer Reiki sessions. She also gave interviews to a variety of newspapers, including in Hawai'i, which gives us some insight into her purposes, at least as far as the interviews can be believed. These need to be taken with a large grain of salt, both because Mrs. Takata always kept her own counsel and because one never knows what the reporter heard and changed before the final article was printed. Even today it is challenging to have Real Reiki® written about correctly by someone who has not studied it.

In 1974, Takata was profiled in the *Honolulu Advertiser*:

"Mrs. Takata plans to teach Reiki until Dec. 24, 1977, and if she can find a successor she hopes to build a Reiki Center on the three acres of land she owns in Olaa, near Kurtistown, Hawaii. In the event she cannot find a capable replacement, the lot will be turned over to the county of Honolulu."[140]

Mrs. Takata was always consistent that she had a secret which made Reiki work, saying even in 1939 that there was a special technique she "mastered" before returning to Hawaii to offer Reiki.[141] World War II obviously changed how publicly she talked about a special "Japanese" secret. However, now that she had reached her seventies, it was clearly time to find a successor. In one 1974 interview, she was quoted as saying, "No one will say it's a shame that Takata took her secret with her."[142] This must have presented her with a dilemma. In Japanese tradition, esoteric secrets usually needed to be passed to one and only one person who would carry the responsibility for that secret knowledge into the next generation.

How could Mrs. Takata decide who the right person was? In the 1970's, a lot of the people who were interested in Reiki were also doing crystal healing, channeling, tarot, massage, shiatsu, aromatherapy, and the whole smorgasbord of trends of the time. They also were learning about gurus. The Beatles had only recently gone public about their study of TM® with the Maharishi. A number of Americans undertook spiritual pilgrimages to India (including a young man named Steve Jobs). Westerners were flocking to all things Eastern. Some changed their Western names to adopt an Eastern persona: for example, a man named Richard Alpert became Ram Dass as part of his spiritual journey.

Reiki was an intriguing Eastern-type method which you could learn in the United States in a weekend in your own hometown – no need to spend months in India or go to some ashram. Some people who took a Reiki class also saw the potential to use Reiki to become gurus themselves.

In the midst of all the alternative and New Age methods available, Mrs. Takata was adamant about the value and merit of Reiki. In a 1974 television interview on the *Don Robb Show* in Honolulu[143], she said

> "I have worked most every day of my life including holidays. Now I am advancing in years and reaching maturity and I feel that I should teach more to many, many people of this noble art because it has been proven all these years."

Mrs. Takata had a challenge as she got older. Remember that each certificate from Dr. Hayashi mentioned "secret": secret knowledge, secret principles. Mrs. Takata kept most of what she learned secret throughout her life, as she was taught. She was fierce in her protection of the intact system she felt had saved her life. What she learned from Dr. Hayashi was kept secret in every way she knew how. Sometimes that meant telling stories to deflect too many questions. Other times it meant giving different bits of information to different people, never letting them know there was anything else to know. Mrs. Takata was actively taking the next steps to find a successor for her secrets without actually revealing those secrets before she found the right person.

Consider for a moment: what if you knew the secret recipe for Kentucky Fried Chicken, and you wanted to find one single person to trust with that recipe? Only you know how many ingredients are in the recipe, and only you know how to put those ingredients together to make perfectly-cooked KFC. In the Western business world, there are processes involved in finding the right person to trust. There are contracts to put the intention into outer form of the one who owns the recipe and the one receiving the secret recipe. However, once those ingredients and that sequence of steps to cook the chicken are out, there is no taking them back. As Benjamin Franklin famously said, "Three may keep a secret, if two of them are dead."[144] Note the recipe for Kentucky Fried Chicken is in fact a famous trade secret: whatever method the KFC company has used to protect their trade secret, it is both famous and has been successful for decades.[145]

Mrs. Takata chose an Eastern way of figuring out whom to trust with the secrets of Reiki. One way to learn what someone would do if they had a secret is to tell them part of the secret, not tell them there is any more of the secret, and then see what they do with what they have. This was a way to test her students without their knowing they were being tested.

Mrs. Takata had been tested in a similar way when she studied with Dr. Hayashi in Japan. When she was assigned to go use Reiki with clients in the afternoons, she had no idea for months that she was being tested, from what she did in the appointments themselves all the way to how well she found her way around Tokyo. Remember, she did not speak very much Japanese, so even getting on trains and finding addresses was not easy. As she told it,

"It was timed. And then the party will telephone and say Takata arrived here at this certain time, and then she left now, she gave me this, and what kind of treatments she gave. That was my examination. I was being checked all the time. I didn't know that until later, very, very late. They said, 'We have tested you already....' He [Dr. Hayashi] said, 'You were following Reiki and Reiki gave you the lead. You never missed one patient. You never came back.

Those are the tests....' And whatever he said I did, I did well."[146]

Mrs. Takata created a similar situation to test students who might become her successor. She already had told only part of what she knew over the years. In some regions, she taught Reiki and never mentioned there even was a Second Degree.[147] In other visits or in private classes, she would talk about the option of Second Degree, but not more. In the 1970's, Mrs. Takata first publicly offered the opportunity for students to become a "Reiki Master" – Third Degree – and be able to activate in others the connection to use universal energy with someone else. What she did not say is what she actually gave a student. She did not give each person the same, or even necessarily all, the information needed to attune someone else to the First or Second Degrees.[148]

This is a very difficult concept for most Westerners. Mrs. Takata charged money for someone to become a "Reiki Master." How could she take money for something and not give them the same thing another person got when they paid for that same thing? From Mrs. Takata's point of view, this was the ultimate test. She did in fact "make" Reiki Masters – contrary to one of the common stories online, she did not have a list of the magical "22 masters" – but many of these "masters" either were not taught all the correct Attunements to attune someone to the First Degree, or did not even learn all the component parts of any Attunement. When Mrs. Takata found out someone claimed to attune a student when they did not have the capacity, she made a special point to fix the error personally, even traveling to where the student was in order to be very clear with everyone involved.[149]

In December 1976, Mrs. Takata sent out a Christmas letter announcing she was retiring in January 1977. She gave the names of three people whom she had "created to carry on this noble work." Notice she still did not say they were her successors: "this noble work" is a very broad and vague category.[150] However, Mrs. Takata in fact did *not* retire in

1977. She continued to observe what the "Reiki Masters" she had taught were doing.

Sometime around 1976 or 1977, Mrs. Takata moved permanently to an apartment in Keosauqua, Iowa, near her daughter Alice and her son-in-law Dr. Kiyoshi Furumoto. Some of Mrs. Takata's surviving friends and relatives in Hawaii had died in the mid-1970's. She herself was having physical issues. She did not leave records of the arguments which convinced her to move from her lifelong home in the balmy islands of Hawai'i to the snowy small town of Keosauqua. Not surprisingly, it was quite a culture shock for her.[151] The local grocery even had to place special orders for fresh fruits and vegetables, especially during the winter: Iowa in the late 1970's was not known for its vast array of Hawaiian fare.

In Keosauqua, Mrs. Takata continued to have a Reiki studio and work with people who needed her help. In 1978, she had her Hawaiian real estate moved into a trust, with a company to administer it.[152] She still traveled to teach classes, although she also was very actively overseeing the people she had told *were* "Reiki Masters." There were numerous letters to and from Mrs. Takata about students, classes, outreach and people who needed help.

Virginia Samdahl, one of the "Reiki Masters" whom Mrs. Takata had partially trained, traveled and taught quite a bit. At a conference, she gave a lecture about Reiki which was attended by a young college professor in Atlanta named Dr. Barbara Weber (later named Dr. Barbara Ray, which name is used herein for clarity). Dr. Ray took Samdahl's First Degree class shortly thereafter and immediately asked Samdahl who had the rest of this technique. Dr. Ray herself had a deep interest in esoteric and ancient systems. She had doctorates in Classics (Greek and Roman) and Art History. Her cross-disciplinary doctoral dissertation was "A Comparative Study of the Dido Theme in Virgil, Ovid and Chaucer," examining the role of the mythic Dido in many interpretations.[153] As a teacher of both art history and mythology, she had delved into the records of the mystery schools of ancient Greece and Rome, the esoteric codes behind Renaissance art, and much more. This background gave Dr. Ray the expertise to recognize the possibility that Reiki was one of those esoteric sciences still extant.

After months of discussion, Virginia Samdahl contacted Mrs. Takata to ask whether she would be willing to talk to this student, Dr. Barbara Weber [Ray]. Dr. Ray mailed her four-page resume to Mrs. Takata, and they began to have telephone conversations.[154] Mrs. Takata then issued a special invitation for Dr. Ray to visit her in Iowa. In August 1979, before the school semester started, Dr. Ray flew from Atlanta to Iowa.

As Dr. Ray has told the story, both privately and in meetings with students of Real Reiki®, when she first arrived at the entrance to Mrs. Takata's apartment, Mrs. Takata faced Dr. Ray, bowed with her hands together in front of her chest, and said, "You're the one I've been waiting for." At that time, Dr. Ray really had no idea what Mrs. Takata meant. Dr. Ray also observed over time that Mrs. Takata did not say that to other people — it was not a strange kind of standard greeting. Throughout her lifetime Mrs. Takata mentioned she had a gift of clairvoyance: one explanation which really fits this circumstance is she had finally found the successor she had been waiting for and talking about for years. Dr. Ray was indeed the person Mrs. Takata had been looking for and waiting for.

Mrs. Takata met with Dr. Ray for extended times, both at Mrs. Takata's home in Iowa and at Dr. Ray's home in Georgia. Mrs. Takata taught Dr. Ray everything she knew about Reiki. Most importantly, she passed the Keys to Reiki to Dr. Barbara Ray. However, she also asked Dr. Ray to hold in silence the information that there even was this entire set of keys until she, Mrs. Takata, had made her transition. She told Dr. Ray that she knew Reiki could and should be presented in an "American" way, but that she, Mrs. Takata, could not do it.

In Mrs. Takata's writing and interviews, she more often vaguely referenced "secrets" in relation to Reiki. In what documentation is available today, nearly forty years after her death, there seems to be only one reference to "keys" and possibly to there being more than three degrees. In that television interview on the *Don Robb Show* in 1974, the transcript reads (about her own study of Reiki), "I got the first degree, the second degree and the third degree – then you become a Master or Healer – then you are handed down the secret and that is the Great Secret."[155] When you know there are in fact seven degrees, you know for once Mrs. Takata went beyond what she usually revealed: after the Third Degree, there is "the Great Secret" of all the degrees in the science. We know from Mrs. Takata's accounts of her study with Dr. Hayashi that she learned to teach others First Degree (that is, she was trained to the Third Degree) when she was still in Japan. Only when Dr. Hayashi visited Hawaii was Mrs. Takata trained in "everything else." The phrase "everything else" again alludes to the fact that there was more to learn than three degrees. Later in that same Don Robb interview, Mrs. Takata also uses the term "key" in reference to someone learning Reiki: "...you have to have a personal contact with the Master. He holds the key and after he tunes you into the Great Energy and Force then it is very simple...."[156]

As an observer of history, it is interesting that before Mrs. Takata's death, no one talked about more than three degrees of Reiki. It was not even an issue: Mrs. Takata offered First Degree for most of her life and only began talking about Third Degree in the 1970's when looking for her successor. In early 1982, the publication of the very first edition of *The Official Reiki Handbook*, Dr. Barbara Ray included a statement which for the first time mentions more degrees in print:

> "The levels beyond the Third Degree contain also the knowledge of how to initiate a full Reiki Master. Dr. Barbara Weber Ray was fully trained in all these levels of Reiki by Master Hawayo Takata prior to

her transition in 1980."[157]

As Mrs. Takata requested, Dr. Ray had not spoken about the other degrees until Mrs. Takata's death. No one during Mrs. Takata's lifetime other than Mrs. Takata herself knew about a fourth degree of Reiki. She did not talk about the complete system or all seven degrees until she shared that information with Dr. Ray in the process of training her to be Mrs. Takata's successor. However, in a rather unbelievable twist, after Dr. Ray made the Fourth Degree available publicly in the mid-1980's, some people offering "reiki things" (things which were *not* the intact science and *not* what Mrs. Takata knew) suddenly announced they could teach a fourth degree.[158]

Mrs. Takata was fierce in her protection of the secrets to Reiki. At the same time, her extreme measures contributed to a fair amount of the chaos surrounding the topic today. The next chapters trace these developments in greater detail.

10 "KEEP THE REIKI PURE"

One of Mrs. Takata's important directions, especially later in the 1970's, was "keep the Reiki pure." Even without extensive education, she knew that if those she taught Reiki added other things in, things which were not part of the intact system, it would not survive for future generations. One of the qualifications she was looking for in a successor was someone who would make Reiki available to Americans, and by extension to Westerners, and keep it unchanged and unaltered for future generations.

When Mrs. Takata trained someone to be a "Reiki Master," she "often told them they would be able to 'make a teacher.' But, she also told them that would not happen 'until she told them.' This would enable her to train them."[159] Although the intact science allows for the attunement processes to be directed to someone not physically present, Mrs. Takata clearly felt strongly enough about Reiki being done right that in at least one case, "upon hearing that a Third Degree Reiki Master had 'supposedly' attuned another person to the Third Degree, she took a plane and flew to the location where this event occurred and herself attuned the person to the Third Degree. Remember that she had all Seven Degrees and knew there were more Degrees and Attunement Processes."[160] She did not reveal everything she knew about Reiki to those "Reiki Masters;" and she kept very careful watch over what these prospective successors were actually doing.

Throughout the increased availability and use of Reiki throughout the United States in the mid to late 1970's, few people understood what Reiki actually was. There was a profusion of "alternative" and "New Age" methods being offered around the country. Reiki looked like yet another kind of psychic healing. Astronaut Edgar Mitchell, one of the astronauts on the Apollo 14 mission and the sixth man to walk on the moon, had considerable involvement with the consciousness movement. In his introduction to Sally Hammond's *We Are All Healers*, he offered the following view of psychic healing:

"But psychic abilities, even healing abilities, do not necessarily equate to spiritual enlightenment, as Miss Hammond has indicated. This lesson has been sounded over and over in the history of psychical research. The reason is simple: psychic energy, like all physical energy, is devoid of an inherent value system. It can be used as the consciousness of the person directing it desires."[161]

Using Mitchell's assessment of the scope of psychic healing, it is even clearer that Reiki is not a psychic healing technique. Real Reiki®, the intact science Mrs. Takata used, gives direct access to universal energy regardless of the consciousness level of the person using it.

Mitchell continues with a caveat that the healing methods discussed in *We Are All Healers* should be considered as "an adjunct to conventional medicine."[162] As previously discussed, Real Reiki® is much more than a "healing" technique. However, in the 1970's, there was no other category in which to put this thing Takata did called Reiki. This led to some confusion, some of which is perpetuated today.

According to a 1974 article, Mrs. Takata was working on a book called *Look Younger, Feel Stronger and a Way to*

Longevity.[163] There are no drafts of such a book in her surviving papers. At this point, she had students who were writers attempting to get articles into the newspapers about Reiki. One such attempt was aimed at the *National Enquirer*: "I chose the Enquirer because not too many magazines are interested in Metaphysics and the Enquirer has a mass audience."[164] However, a different student had no luck with the same magazine, writing,

"Well I have tried my best with all the possible ways I could think of the [sic] keep the article on you and Reiki alive. But it seems National Enquirer is very strict about having all the facts varified [sic]. Especially something to do with AMA [American Medical Association]. Something of that nature could cause lawsuits against the paper."[165]

This was in the 1970's; today the standards and studies necessary to label something "medical" or "healing" are even more stringent.

Mrs. Takata did start several drafts of other books throughout her life. The first is a five-page typewritten manuscript from approximately 1948 of something called "The Art of Healing." It is part explanation of Reiki, and part notes about specific hand positions for certain conditions.[166] Many years later, Dr. Barbara Ray included a longer and fuller section of conditions at the end of the first published handbook for Reiki practitioners, *The Official Reiki Handbook*. This book is now in its fourth edition, *The Official Handbook of The Radiance Technique®, Authentic Reiki®*, while the list of conditions is in its own 309-page book, *The New Expanded Reference Manual of The Radiance Technique®, Authentic Reiki®*. *The New Expanded Reference Manual* is a reference for using TRT® with everything from Aardvark to Zest, complete with entries for things like "Cell Phone" and "Social Networking" which Mrs. Takata never lived long enough to experience.

There are several drafts, both handwritten and typed, of what could be called Mrs. Takata's autobiography. All the versions combine stories about her life, the legend of Dr.

Usui and anecdotes about using Reiki with a large variety of people and conditions. At least one of the typewritten mid-1970's versions seems to be a transcription of her speaking on tape, since she had correspondence about completing the transcripts.[167] All the versions – from 1973 through the audio tapes she recorded in December 1979 – have many of the same stories told virtually in the same words. It is clear Mrs. Takata loved telling a good story and that she had crafted many of them over years. Students of Mrs. Takata remember hearing some of the same stories, in the same words, when she was teaching.[168]

What this collection of autobiographical drafts also shows is how important Mrs. Takata felt it was to have a book about Reiki. She knew putting the information in published form was one way to help "keep the Reiki pure." None of her attempts made it to book form. However, the impetus was very strong in her to find someone who would truly understand Reiki and be her successor to make it available. As she said in a 1974 interview, "When I pass on, they won't say that Takata was great but she took her knowledge with her. I want to leave it behind for everyone."[169]

Although Dr. Ray did not know it at the time, she was the one, as Mrs. Takata said, who she had been waiting for. Mrs. Takata officially attuned Dr. Barbara Ray to the Third Degree as a Reiki Master on September 1, 1979. A letter Dr. Ray wrote to Mrs. Takata on September 4 begins, "There are no words to express the honor and privilege of spending the week with you as a student and as a guest – thank you so very, very much – I am deeply grateful and honored."[170] Later that month, Mrs. Takata wrote a response to Dr. Barbara Ray which also followed up on their conversations in person:

> "You have inspired me to no end, and it gives me the opportunity to open my heart to you. For some years, I have started to write my experiences (40 years or more) about Reiki. My desire is, it has to be

a worthy one to publish, and to pass on to the readers that Reiki is deep, deep and not many can fathom, nor grasp its beauty, nor know the value to everything that has Life. If you accept and willing to help me, please have some spare time this winter, I would like to sit down with you and accomplish, the desire. In the past, many has offered their kindness, even professional writers have offered their services, but I could not go to any writers, who were not a student of Reiki. They must know the real taste, bite it, chew it, digest it, but non-students will never know the true taste, only words."[171]

Hawayo Takata (c. 1978)

In December 1979, Dr. Ray spent two weeks in Iowa studying with Mrs. Takata and recording Mrs. Takata's memoirs and stories in preparation for a book. Mrs. Takata was absolutely clear that accurate information needed to be available for students and the public. This was part of her way to "keep the Reiki pure": if the information was published, it would be more difficult for people to add to or change what she had taught.

Already, by 1978 and 1979, Mrs. Takata had been extremely disappointed in some of the people she had called "Reiki Masters." A husband and wife who were ministers (of the metaphysical variety) in California had often hosted Mrs. Takata for lectures and classes. The man was actually one of three people Mrs. Takata listed in 1976 as "carrying on the noble work," although she never called those students her successors. However, in a letter dated May 10, 1979, Mrs. Takata wrote,

"I hear all kinds of rumors, looks like everyone wants to write a book after few months of Reiki lessons_and always some Reiki teach pops up_The [couple — *names redacted*] are a dissappointment [sic]..."[172]

She continues with a number of troubling personal allegations, and concludes, "If it is true, it is very unbecoming for a church minister...Truly she is NOT a Reiki Master."[173]

From an historical perspective, it is not surprising that some of the people who flocked to Reiki proceeded to do things which, from Mrs. Takata's point of view, did *not* "keep the Reiki pure." Overall, these were people who already had a student base, who taught channeling or crystals or tarot cards or Eastern mysticism or any number of other modalities. They also did not understand the value of Reiki as its own method: they wanted to use Reiki as part of their collection of techniques and beliefs. Most of all, they tended to be people who saw becoming a "Reiki Master" as a path to becoming a guru.

11 THE SEARCH FOR A SUCCESSOR

Mrs. Takata often said she was going to live to be 100. In 1980, she was 79 years old. She was still traveling, although she claimed it was less than previously, and working on getting her book about Reiki into shape. A letter in January 1980 confirmed the work was progressing on the tapes she recorded in December 1979: "It is indeed an honor to be writing to you and to be associated with Reiki. It is also an honor to be helping Barbara Weber [Ray] with the typing of your tapes into manuscript form."[174]

Remember Mrs. Takata had said in her Christmas 1976 letter that she was retiring. In the first two months of 1980, she traveled at least to Phoenix, Arizona; San Mateo, California; Hilo, Hawai'i (to observe the first anniversary of her sister's death); Kauai; Honolulu; and Colorado. She planned to go to Tampa, St. Petersburg and Orlando in March, followed by Atlanta on April 1. In Atlanta she was going to see the dogwood festival, visit Dr. Ray and her Reiki Center, and consult a lawyer "to patent Reiki, so no one can abuse it or call [it] their own. Of course I will have to spend money for fees, but this is to protect my book too which is being processed there with Barbara's help."[175]

As it turned out, Mrs. Takata did not complete this

extensive itinerary. She became ill and did not go to Florida or Georgia in the spring. The appointment with the lawyer did not happen, which had a profound effect later. However, as she wrote in June, "Reiki put me back on my feet."[176]

Seemingly recovered, in August she traveled first to Stockton (California) and then did indeed go to Atlanta. During that extended visit, she stayed with Dr. Ray in Dr. Ray's home. Mrs. Takata visited the new Reiki Center and celebrated the new organization founded for all Reiki students: the American Reiki Association, Inc. Dr. Ray also hosted a lecture for Mrs. Takata to which hundreds of people came. After the lecture, Mrs. Takata stood for hours and talked to each person who stood in line to meet her, only leaving when the hotel management told them they needed to close the hall for the night.[177]

Hawayo Takata & Dr. Barbara Ray (August 1980)

Mrs. Takata knew she was not doing well physically.[178] She had started looking seriously for a successor in the early 1970's and had not been happy about what her possible successors chose to do with Reiki. When Dr. Ray visited her for the first time, Mrs. Takata bowed to her and said, "You're the one I've been waiting for." She may well have known she was running out of time to find a trustworthy and appropriate person to whom to give her secrets. Her actions in 1980 show her increasingly urgent need to pass her secrets before she died.

Throughout her life, her family was central to Mrs. Takata's life. The Japanese overall have a deep respect for family, with religious beliefs interwoven with reverence for one's ancestors. From the early deaths of some of her siblings to her caring for and supporting both her parents and daughters as a young widow, Mrs. Takata was very involved in her family's life and welfare. Even her connections in Japan which led to her discovering Reiki were threaded through with family connections. The doctor she chose to consult in Japan had been a friend of her husband, Saichi. That doctor called his sister to take Mrs. Takata to Dr. Hayashi's clinic. Even Dr. Hayashi's visit to Hawaii was ostensibly motivated by his daughter, Kiyoe, visiting Hawaii before the responsibilities of marriage precluded her travel. For her entire lifetime, Mrs. Takata maintained strong ties to all generations of her family, including the extended Takata family.

This strong connection of course included her daughter, Alice Furumoto, and Alice's children, whom she visited periodically in Iowa. Remember, though, that for all but the last few years of her life, Mrs. Takata lived and worked in Hawaii, while Alice had moved away from Hawaii shortly after the war and soon after settled with her husband in Iowa. Their lives were very different.

When Dr. Ray visited Mrs. Takata in Iowa, Mrs. Takata's daughter Alice had picked her up at the airport for the long drives back and forth to Keosauqua. In those drives, Alice made it very clear that she did not want any of her children "indoctrinated" into Reiki, and that she had been trying to get her mother to stop doing Reiki.[179] There is no way to know all of Alice's reasons. It is certainly understandable if, being a part of the only family of Asian ancestry in that small town, Alice had been trying through the decades to keep anything "weird" from singling her family out.

Despite Alice's lectures to Dr. Ray, by the time Mrs. Takata wrote letters to her granddaughter Phyllis in 1980, Mrs. Takata herself was emphatic about Phyllis learning how to do what her grandmother did. In February 1980, Mrs. Takata became explicit about providing her granddaughter with an inheritance. After telling Phyllis about the work she was doing on her book and her plans to see a lawyer to "patent Reiki," she wrote, "I am doing all this so that I can retire and turn over to you on a silver platter and enjoy and become a #1 Reiki Master."[180] Later, in June, she wrote another letter about how to do a lecture, sign up students, what to pay the coordinator of the lecture/class, and what to teach each day of a First Degree class.[181] It is fairly obvious reading it that she was trying to begin teaching Phyllis about Reiki by mail since Phyllis was not going to visit her and in fact was going to Alaska.

Invitation to reception in Atlanta, Georgia (1980)

During Mrs. Takata's August 1980 stay in Atlanta, she asked Dr. Ray directly to teach Phyllis if Mrs. Takata was no longer there.[182] She also requested Dr. Ray to promise not to speak about the Keys to Reiki until Mrs. Takata's death, and Dr. Ray did so promise.[183] In meetings with students in Atlanta, Mrs. Takata announced that Dr. Barbara Ray was to be "the initiating teacher." As further detailed in a letter from the A.R.A. Board of Directors, Mrs. Takata "told her [Dr. Ray] not to tell anyone or to make a Master until she dies. We cannot really know or question the reasoning as to why Master Takata did not share with the other teachers this information."[184]

At the end of that August visit, Dr. Ray drove Mrs. Takata to the airport, where Mrs. Takata had her drive around the departures area twice before telling her to stop. Mrs. Takata got out of the car with her luggage and obtained a skycap to help her. At no time did she say where she was going or even indicate what airline she was flying on.[185] Evidence from one of her letters – written in larger and shakier writing than in previous months – suggests she flew to Portland from Atlanta.[186] However, her daughter Alice called Dr. Ray asking where her mother was, as if she had been expected back in Iowa. Mrs. Takata clearly was still determined to keep her secrets and to travel when and where she chose.

Soon after that Atlanta visit, Dr. Ray wrote to Mrs. Takata:

"I am so deeply filled with gratitude for all you have done for Reiki for so many years of your life. Your strength is beautiful and an inspiration to me.

I am dedicating my life to Reiki and will follow your ideals and meet the challenges of the future years with your strength in me."[187]

Hawayo Hiromi Takata made her transition out of this life on December 11, 1980 at 2:45 a.m. in the hospital in Keosauqua, Iowa. There were no cell phones and no emails, so the news did not spread as quickly as it does now. Dr. Ray herself had gone to Italy for the Christmas break from the university where she taught, and she did not hear until her return in January.

Hawayo Takata wearing A.R.A. T-shirt (1980)

"The Reiki Review," published by the American Reiki Association (A.R.A.), issued its first newsletter in Spring 1981 with a large front-page notice:

"IN MEMORIAL
MASTER HAWAYO TAKATA
Dec. 23, 1900 - Dec. 11, 1980

It is with deep honor and respect that we announce the transition of Master Hawayo Takata and dedicate this issue to her memory.

We are filled with Gratitude for her life's journey which brought the Gift of Reiki to the Western world." [188]

In August 1980, Mrs. Takata had also given a list of the "Reiki Masters" she had partially trained to Dr. Ray. Soon after Mrs. Takata's death, Dr. Ray, as president of the A.R.A., sent a letter to each of these students of Mrs. Takata's to invite them to participate in the outreach of Reiki and all the benefits of a national organization. The letter, dated February 8, 1981, gives quite a bit of information and extends an expansive invitation. With permission, the first half of this letter is reproduced below:

"In honor of the memory of Master Hawayo Takata, may we serve to carry on Reiki to its Highest Potential. May her Soul achieve its Rightful Unfolding. We are filled with Gratitude for all that she has Given.

"For the past fourteen months, I have with the guidance and advice of Master Takata, by letters and phone calls, worked to establish the American Reiki Association. She had, in Dec. 1979, agreed to act as the Special Advisor to the A.R.A. When Master Takata came to Atlanta in August, 1980 for two weeks, among many of her treasured activities both public and private was her presence as the Guest of Honor at a Reception for those who had taken Reiki in this area to meet with her. Approximately 200 people attended this event at which Master Takata officially announced the founding of the American Reiki Association. She also presented for public display the official 'logo' of the A.R.A. which has been legally registered with the proper government agency. She shared publically her support of the A.R.A. and expressed her pleasure that this organization was now in progress for the future of Reiki. Her visit to Atlanta was indeed an historic event for Reiki in modern times.

"What is the American Reiki Association? The

A.R.A. is a not-for-profit national, membership organization for all students of Reiki. The A.R.A. was modelled by our attorneys after other reputable membership organizations such as the American Medical Association. The purposes of the A.R.A. are many and include providing membership, publishing the Reiki Review to share ideas and experiences pertaining to Reiki and healing, establishing and maintaining a Code of Ethics, promoting Reiki in a professional manner, informing the public about Reiki and establishing standards for Reiki teachers in the future.

"Following the advice of Master Takata, the A.R.A. is forming an ongoing Special Adjunct Committee composed of all Reiki Masters whose appointment to that committee is life-long. Therefore, as the current President of A.R.A., I am inviting you to be a member of this Special Committee and am asking you to accept or decline in writing to the A.R.A. The purposes of this committee will, of course, unfold as we move into the future. However, your input for the Code of Ethics is needed now with a deadline of March 15, 1981. Once your suggestions have been assembled, you will be sent copies for review and advise...."[189]

Unfortunately, it seems a number of the people who had paid Mrs. Takata to become a "Reiki Master" were not at all interested in this offer. Some of them, especially those who had been successful as "Reiki Masters" before Mrs. Takata's death, apparently saw no reason to work in cooperation with anyone else. The A.R.A. was not requiring anyone to participate. However, if Reiki was to become more public and available in the U.S. and elsewhere, it was important to be consistent and professional in the way Reiki was presented to the public.

12 MASTERS AND LINEAGE

Mrs. Takata used the term "Reiki Master." However, her use of it seems to be far more changeable with the context. Notice that in one case Mrs. Takata wrote regretfully about someone's bad behavior and inappropriate actions, and then concluded, "she is NOT a Reiki Master." To Mrs. Takata, the use of the term "Reiki Master" was not a title, a description of educational achievement or even solely about level of study: "Reiki Master" was more a complex relationship involving the entire person.

Her use of the term "Reiki Master" seems to be one example of language which has subtext as part of what is being said. Even though Hawayo Takata was legally born an American citizen, she was raised in a strongly Japanese culture and learned Reiki in Japan. Her cultural roots were definitely Japanese. Even today there are major differences between American cultural behaviors and those of the Japanese. With the globalization of business and worldwide communication, those differences are more identified and examined. In the 1970's there would have been limited recognition of how deep these differences can go.

To start, Americans and Japanese have almost

diametrically opposed styles of communication. In Erin Meyer's excellent examination of unconscious patterns within cultures, *The Culture Map*, she labels these styles "low-context" and "high-context."[190] In a low-context style, good communication "is precise, simple, and clear. Messages are expressed and understood at face value." This is the general American default. On the other hand, high-context communication "is sophisticated, nuanced, and layered. Messages are both spoken and read between the lines. Messages are often implied but not clearly expressed." This is the Japanese (among other cultures) default. As Meyer states directly (in a low-context, explicit style), "If you're from a low-context culture, you may perceive a high-context communicator as secretive, lacking transparency, or unable to communicate effectively."[191] Mrs. Takata without question was what Americans – and most Westerners – would call secretive and lacking transparency. Her use of the term "Reiki Master" is consistent with that bias towards "high-context" communication, where much is implied or embedded within the communication and never said directly.

Dr. Barbara Ray, an American, addresses the term "Reiki Master" from another, more direct and low-context perspective. "The term Reiki Master was never intended to differentiate the person with the title as an enlightened being."[192] Rather, the level of study – Third Degree for Teaching, being able to teach another person First Degree – includes the tools which give you the *potential* of becoming a master of energy.

Nonetheless, in the years that Mrs. Takata offered the opportunity for people to become Reiki Masters, the phrase became both a badge of authority and a locus for arguments. The question of who would take over from Mrs. Takata when she died had become more controversial even before Mrs. Takata's death. There seem to have already been fairly extensive rumors in 1980 of some kind of struggle over who was going to be Mrs. Takata's successor. A student of one of the "Reiki Masters" – whom herself had never met Mrs. Takata – felt so strongly about the uncertainties surrounding the future of Reiki that she wrote a letter to Mrs. Takata in July 1980. Her teacher had "told us the story of your wonderful determination in obtaining the teachings and in keeping them pure."[193] She continued with an explanation that she had been doing astrological charts about the future of Reiki and was very concerned, especially as there was a "him" who was claiming he had been designated Mrs. Takata's successor when he definitely had not been. She wrote,

"I am to be the one to plead with you to designate a successor, IN WRITING, now....It can easily be said by someone that you have designated him – and who can disprove it, unless you act now to prevent it?"[194]

Mrs. Takata in fact did not write a letter to everyone announcing her successor. In Japanese culture, there is a strong implicit bias towards a hierarchical social order, possibly stemming from the centuries of Confucian influence.[195] Meyer labels this aspect of culture the "Leading" scale, ranging from a very egalitarian leadership style (with Denmark, the Netherlands and Sweden on the far end of egalitarian) to a highly hierarchical chain of command (Japan falling on the extreme edge of this scale).[196] This helps illuminate Mrs. Takata's unshakable belief that no one would say they could do more with Reiki than she had permitted, and that she did not need to make announcements about the Reiki she protected.

Mrs. Takata was the authority on Reiki. In Japanese society, especially a generation or more ago, it would be unthinkable to take an action unsanctioned by your boss or authority figure. In this kind of orderly hierarchical leadership structure, Mrs. Takata had the responsibility for caring for her students; they had the responsibility to follow her directions exactly. In this model, there is no way someone would claim to be her successor without her explicit permission and direction to do so. In the more egalitarian, democratic American culture of the 1970's, this Japanese structure was almost incomprehensible. Americans thought once Mrs. Takata said they were a Reiki Master, they could pretty much do whatever they wanted.

As part of her hierarchical cultural view, Mrs. Takata believed strongly in the importance of taking care of family. It was in her August 1980 visit to Atlanta that Mrs. Takata requested Dr. Ray train her granddaughter, Phyllis Furumoto.[197] In 1980, Phyllis was 32 years old. She had been a ski instructor and never been very interested in Reiki, as her mother, Alice had tried to ensure. However, after her grandmother's death and with the push from the A.R.A. to make Reiki widely available, Phyllis became more interested. Her mother, Alice, also seems to have discovered how important her mother was after Mrs. Takata's death. In a collection of her reminders after her mother's death, with memos about eulogies and things to do with her mother's papers and possible book, Alice wrote in a stream-of-consciousness comment to herself, "She has left her legacy to Phyllis. And as Phyllis matures... her growth with Reiki... shall she inherit?"[198] Note that Phyllis at this point was in her mid-30's: the fact that her mother was still waiting for Phyllis to mature says something about the situation, too.

Very quickly after Mrs. Takata's death, the confusion about what she had said and whom she taught became widespread. Some people who had been partially trained by Mrs. Takata chose to change the name of what they did and no longer called it "Reiki." In those cases, there was no conflict. Others wanted to teach their own versions of Reiki and rode the wave of popularity created by the A.I.R.A. expansion and advertising, taking advantage of standards and qualifications they themselves did not have. This caused increasing confusion for the public, which did not know about an intact science compared to things people made up. Reiki was brought to the West by Mrs. Takata; person A says she studied with Mrs. Takata; how would a student know there was anything more to ask?

Physicist David Bohm spent a lifetime exploring the interrelationships of quantum physics and consciousness. He examined deeply the human powers of observation and differentiation. In his classic book *Wholeness and the Implicate Order*, he points to exactly this kind of confusion and conflict when people are not clear observers:

> "*To be confused about what is different and what is not, is to be confused about everything.* Thus, it is not an accident that our fragmentary form of thought is leading to such a widespread range of crises, social, political, economic, ecological, psychological, etc., in the individual and in society as a whole. Such a mode of thought implies unending development of chaotic and meaningless conflict...."[199]

The insistence of those who were partially trained by Mrs. Takata refusing to understand there was more to the science than they had been told led to much of the problems of differentiation today.

Phyllis Furumoto probably caused the most chaos around "reiki" in those first years. There is a fair amount of evidence about Phyllis's decisions after her grandmother's death. As Carell Ann Farmer, a woman Phyllis "made a Reiki Master," shared in an open letter in 1997,

> "I met Phyllis shortly after her grandmother, Hawayo Takata died. Over a period of several years (1981 - 1984) we were in close association. Phyllis confided in me. She talked to me in great detail of her confusion over her grandmother's death, her grandmother's lack of clarifying Phyllis's future role, her lack of direction in her own life and her fear of the opportunity that was before her to step forward into the position that her grandmother had filled.
>
> "I remember the day that she arrived at my house and pronounced that she had made a decision. Her

decision was clear. She said, 'I will go for the money.' She had decided to pursue her grandmother's work – teaching classes, initiating Masters – for the income potential. She initiated four Masters between Feb. 1981 and April 1982. She began to plan the first gathering of Reiki Masters in Hawaii (April 1982) and the memorial service for her grandmother."[200]

Meanwhile, after Mrs. Takata's death, Dr. Ray had been writing and calling Phyllis, trying to fulfill the promise to Mrs. Takata to train Phyllis to become a Reiki Master. Phyllis seemed not to understand that there were actual formulas or keys which had to be correct and intact in order for the Attunements to work. In October 1981, Phyllis visited Dr. Ray in Atlanta. While she was there, she said directly to Nonie Greene that she had not gotten any keys from her grandmother.[201] At the same time, she refused to change what she was telling people about Reiki, claiming she could create "Reiki Masters" anyway. In 1983, Phyllis wrote to Dr. Ray, "I do appreciate the clearness and recent communication from you. I intend to convey to you my basic belief system of Reiki so that we may have an understanding of each other."[202] One of her statements in this letter really reveals her profound misunderstanding of the science of Real Reiki®:

"The relationship between the student and teacher is a bond that makes it possible for the Reiki energy to be accepted by the student. This relationship is one of magic and of circumstance. The student comes to a class on the Usui System by a personal connection and of a commitment of the right moment in growth."[203]

Mrs. Takata had formulas. Even when she did not say much about the science, she spoke about formulas and something special she had to do to give her students the capacity to use Reiki. It was never necessary to do some kind of magic or to have the energy "accepted" by anyone.

Sadly, Phyllis seemed to have a very emotional attachment to what she thought she understood. Her explanation for why she would not agree to learn more about Reiki: "Takata told me I have everything I need in Reiki. To deny that statement would be to deny my teacher. I cannot do that. She gave me different things than anyone else — and everyone else received things I did not."[204] Mrs. Takata may well have said Phyllis had everything she needed in Reiki... but that was not the same as saying that she knew everything about the inner workings of the science. Another person trained by Mrs. Takata wrote to Phyllis as a "reporting and feedback communique" and quotes a conversation she observed when Phyllis was talking to an interested student. According to this summary,

"What you did say...was — When you [Phyllis] went to Atlanta and sat in BWR's [Barbara Weber Ray's] living room and was told BWR had keys which you did not have, you cried and asked for the other keys, saying, 'How could grandmother shortchange me that way.'"[205]

The person writing to Phyllis was not happy that Phyllis had admitted she did not have the keys from her grandmother.

Rather than continuing with her training as her grandmother had wanted, Phyllis contacted a number of "Reiki Masters" who had been partially taught by Mrs. Takata. They had been trying to decide what they were going to do. This was the beginning of Phyllis's organization, the Reiki Alliance, which was loosely modeled on the A.I.R.A. (except it was only for teachers). The letter by Carell Ann Farmer describes that first meeting after Mrs. Takata's death:

"I sat in the circle at the first gathering of Reiki Masters in Hawaii in 1982. I had been an initiated Master for 10 days. I listened to the stories of how Takata had taught each master differently. We drew the symbols together. It was quite shocking to the group to find out that they were different, similar in some respects and different in others. What did this mean? Discussion around this led to an agreement that we would all use the same symbols. I no longer remember exactly how we determined the correct symbols. It marked the beginning of attempted standardization. Takata's unique method of teaching was a source of great upset...."[206]

Unfortunately, none of the people in that circle grasped that Mrs. Takata told different people different things as part of her protection of the intact science. Farmer, in her letter, explains her belief that the symbols needed to be different for each person, and that using Reiki is a matter of feeling. She clearly feels strongly that each master needs the "freedom to discover their own uniqueness." However, it is the direct, reliable contact with universal energy using the formulas of Real Reiki® which gives each practitioner the real "freedom to discover their own uniqueness." The formulas themselves do not need to be reinvented, just as the recipe for KFC would work for anyone *as long as they knew the secret recipe and could do the processes to create the recipe.*

It is actually somewhat agonizing to observe the personalities who wrote back and forth arguing about almost everything except the keys themselves. Phyllis, as Mrs. Takata's granddaughter and the instigator of resistance to anything beyond what Hawayo Takata said in the public eye, acted as the center of these arguments. Despite the fact that Phyllis said more than once that she had not learned how to attune someone from her grandmother,[207] she claimed that because she was Mrs. Takata's granddaughter, she had the "lineage."

The word "lineage" has become some kind of magic talisman in the thickets of "reiki things." Many people who "do reiki" give a list of people stretching back to Mrs. Takata, as if it were a pedigree or family tree, some extending thirty or forty names into the past. It makes it sound as if what Mrs. Takata did could be passed by some kind of contagion.

The misconception inherent in this concept of a line of descent is to think that someone who simply studied part of the science can actually pass that science on to someone else. Only those who hold the keys can pass them to someone else. A correct "lineage" actually would be to list the people who have held the Keys to Reiki and could attune others to the First through the Seventh Degrees. That lineage is:

Dr. Mikao Usui

Dr. Chujiro Hayashi

Hawayo Takata

Dr. Barbara Ray

The person to whom Dr. Ray passes the intact Keys

Each teacher attuned by one of these masters to the Third Degree could – if they also had the correct formulas – attune others to the First or Second Degrees. Their students, though, have no capacity to attune someone else to any degree. There are formulas pictured online which claim to be Attunements for one degree or another. However, whatever these two-dimensional representations may be, they are not connected to anything and so have no power. The formulas will not work without being connected and tuned to the entire system. It is as if you had a picture of a phone charger and thought by drawing that picture, your phone would be charged.

There are two pieces which need to be in place before a person can attune someone to the First Degree:

1. The person has to have been attuned to teach The First Degree (studied The Third Degree for Teaching)
2. The person has to have learned the correct formulas (attunements) to set up the consistent, reliable connection within another living system

This does not even address the larger issue, which is that Mrs. Takata had the keys to the seven degrees which comprise the entire science. These seven degrees work as an interconnected whole, each one in relation to the whole of the system. In order to be attuned to the Third Degree and be able to attune someone else to use the First Degree, there has to be someone who had studied at least to the Fifth Degree and could attune someone else to the Third Degree. It is orderly, not magic.

To use an analogy, it is as if a concert violinist wanted to play the Mendelssohn Violin Concerto with an orchestra. However, the strings of the violin available cannot be tuned to the same pitch as the orchestra, and the violinist had never learned the piece and does not have the sheet music for it. Without those missing parts, there is no way the violinist will be able to play the concerto with the orchestra. It does not matter how much he wants to play, or knows he is a master violinist, or is told he is capable of doing it and has it within him. Likewise, the person who wants to attune someone else to be able to use Real Reiki® is in a similar position as the would-be soloist: without the missing parts of the whole – 1) alignment/attunement to the whole of the system and 2) the formulas which are part of the system – that person cannot "play with the orchestra." He cannot attune another person to any degree of Real Reiki®.

The complete science is actually very orderly, as explained clearly by Dr. Barbara Ray:

"One attuned to the Seventh Degree has the capacity to attune others to any of the other Degrees, and, only someone attuned properly to the Seventh Degree would have the capacity and inner-connection to attune another person to the Sixth and Fifth Degrees. Likewise, within this system rediscovered by Dr. Usui, it requires someone attuned properly to the Fifth Degree to have the capacity to attune another to the Fourth and Third Degrees. Likewise, from within this system when intact, it requires someone attuned properly to the Third Degree to have the capacity to attune another to the Second and First Degrees."[208]

Every piece of historical evidence shows Mrs. Takata only passed the keys – the formulas – for attuning someone to all Seven Degrees to one person: Dr. Barbara Ray. No one else ever had the formulas to create another Third Degree, what Mrs. Takata called a "Reiki Master." The information about seven degrees was the "Great Secret" kept by Hawayo Takata as part of her method of protecting the intact system.

Some "Reiki Masters," years after Mrs. Takata's death, belatedly claimed they knew another degree or that they had been revealed new symbols in a dream. One can only imagine what Mrs. Takata, who so fiercely protected the "pure" Reiki, would have said to such claims. Dr. Ray knew from her first contact with Reiki that there was more than the First Degree, and most likely, based on her study of ancient esoteric sciences, there would be seven levels. Fortunately for students around the world, Mrs. Takata decided Dr. Ray was the right person to whom to pass the keys. Because Dr. Ray accepted that responsibility, the intact science of Real Reiki®, Authentic Reiki®, TRT® is available today to anyone who wants to learn.

13 FORMULAS, FEELINGS, TOUCH AND BELIEF

While this book is not a primer on the science of Real Reiki® itself, it is helpful to establish a few basic facts. An overview of the intact science and its application can clarify our examination of the history as Real Reiki® spread through the United States, Canada, Europe, South America and Australia.

The science of Real Reiki®, TRT®, is made up of specific formulas in the form of cosmic symbols. These symbols are each aspects of the Whole (refer again to the Energy Model and that point of wholeness pictured at the center of the model). As Dr. Ray describes cosmic symbols, "Different aspects of the whole generate different vibrations which are inner-connected with the resonance of The Whole – The Universe – The Cosmos."[209] The different symbols have different functions within the science of TRT®, just as wires and circuit breakers have different functions within the science of electricity. If you have one part, it will not give you the functionality of the whole; owning a plug does not let you use that plug to charge your phone unless it is correctly connected to the entire system and set up to use the right voltage.

Other transcendental sciences are made of different kinds of component parts. For example, the science of TM® (Transcendental Meditation) is made up of mantras, or sounds which have specific vibrations resonating with the Whole. The science of Yantras consists of formulas which look like complex visual patterns. Each of these sciences has a language which, when used in interaction with living beings, can bring the vibrations of that system into harmony and alignment with universal, whole energy.

Any transcendental science, if intact and complete, has a coherent and consistent set of formulas or vibratory tools which allow us to access that vibration of wholeness. The challenge is that Western scientific methods are well-developed to examine parts, primarily physical parts, and definitely not whole, non-physical energy. For example, microscopes, X-rays, hadron colliders, and fMRI's are designed to measure and/or document specific physical conditions and processes down to the finest level. There is no machine which can identify transcendental energy.

Studying something which cannot be seen has been challenging throughout history. The very study of our solar system required tools better than the naked eye to see there were other planets and not merely brighter and dimmer stars. Before microscopes, no one would have believed there could be little organisms living in a drop of water. In the mid-1800's, Pasteur and Lister proposed a radical theory: bacteria in organic material could cause decay or infection. Fifty years later Einstein catapulted physics into a new, quantum science, in which particles can only be identified based on observing the traces they leave behind. In only the last few years, advances in brain imaging using fMRI's have opened up possibilities of reading thoughts using artificial intelligence algorithms. Each of these discoveries has been a fairly radical departure from science as it was previously understood and practiced.

The studies of astronomy, microbiology, neuroscience and quantum physics all consist of looking at physical matter, even if indirectly on the quantum level. It is not surprising that a science which accesses transcendental – the very word means "beyond the senses" – energy would be very difficult to test and codify.

Students of a transcendental energy science such as Real Reiki®, TRT®, are left with what is called – sometimes derogatorily – anecdotal evidence. After forty-four years of Mrs. Takata's work with Reiki and forty-two years and counting of Dr. Ray's continuing with that intact system, there is of course a very large collection of anecdotal evidence about the use of Reiki, Real Reiki®, in the West. The models and body of knowledge which Dr. Ray created about the science give us a strong framework within which to understand our experiences. Dr. Ray's clarity about differentiating between the science, its applications, and the experiences of its application support further growth and understanding for students each day. Still, sometimes it takes 20/20 hindsight to be able to trace the unfolding healing/wholing process with the application of Real Reiki®, TRT®. The study of Wholeness can be a lifetime of discovery.

For those who learned some kind of "reiki" unconnected to the actual science, it can be very difficult to understand the difference between the intact science and what they learned, usually from someone who seemed well-meaning and sincere. Some "reiki" teachers even use symbols and formulas they got from someone else or from online, and there is no "machine" to measure the fact these symbols have no power. In this era of truth often determined by popular opinion, simply looking up information about "reiki" does not provide much clarification, either.[210]

Almost forty years after Mrs. Takata's death, there is no question that people offering "reiki things" do *not* have direct access to universal, whole energy through the science of Real Reiki®. *If* one or two of the "Reiki Masters" trained by Mrs. Takata before her death in 1980 actually did have both the capacity *and* the formulas to attune someone to the First Degree (which we definitely know was not always the case), those people *never* had the capacity to attune anyone to the Third Degree. Those first students who might have been able to attune only to the First Degree are now dead. Anyone they "trained," who taught others who taught others, had no capacity to access that whole, universal energy. The "reiki things" advertised today are something else, not a transcendental energy science.

Why wouldn't someone be able to tell the difference? First and most obviously, there is no machine which can measure universal, transcendental energy. While it is easy to see whether the light goes on when you flip the switch (meaning your electrical wiring was done correctly and powers a light properly), it is impossible for people to "see" transcendental light. Second, there can definitely be effects and feelings on the outer planes – mental, emotional and physical – from "reiki things," simply as part of our experience as human beings. The effect of touch is powerful. However, human touch is not the same thing as Real Reiki®.

A hands-on application which looks like Mrs. Takata's Reiki consists of gentle touch on at least twelve positions on the head and body, usually for about five minutes per position. Given how restricted touch has become in our society (especially in the United States), any kind of non-invasive, caring touch will probably feel good. In our stressful world, just lying down for an hour and placing your own hands or having someone else put their hands gently on various positions would very likely be relaxing and/or restorative.

Recent research on touch reveals interesting data which also sheds some light on the challenges of differentiation. One psychological experiment examined how a test subject assessed a person based on a list of traits (for example, "intelligent, skillful, industrious, determined, practical and cautious"[211]). In some cases, the test subject had – without their knowing it was part of the study – held a warm cup of coffee shortly before giving their assessment. In other cases, the subject had held a cup of iced coffee. The study showed the subjects who held the warm cup perceived the person being described as "significantly warmer (humane, trustworthy, friendly)"[212] than those who had held the iced coffee. Just the brief, unrelated experience of physical warmth on their hand influenced the test subject's emotional judgement. It is quite likely someone's warm hands gently touching your head or body would feel good, and, from the results of this study, would influence you to think you had gotten benefits from the session.

Another interesting study looked at the behavior of American and French adolescents. The researchers chose two McDonald's in equivalent middle-class areas of Miami and Paris. They observed teens interacting and codified each behavior. The American teens were seen to touch each other far less and do more fidgeting with themselves (twirling their hair, playing with rings, biting their lips) compared to the French teens who leaned on each other, casually touched another's arm, and so on. The American teens also were more aggressive verbally and physically than the French teens.[213] One conclusion which may be drawn from this study is that more positive touching may decrease levels of aggressive behavior.

Of course, the comfort level with and acceptance of touch varies in different countries. There are some studies examining touch in regular daily interactions. One scientist visited cafes in different areas and counted how many times two people sharing coffee touched each other. The results were: London, England, 0; Gainesville, Florida, 2; Paris, France, 110; and San Juan, Puerto Rico, more than 180 touches.[214] Many studies have demonstrated that touch is essential for human beings... and modern society in many places has limited the amount and type of acceptable kinds of touch dramatically.

There are measurable results from touch in more restricted environments. In hospitals, patients whose doctors touched them, even with a gentle touch on the arm, had reduced stress-hormone levels and better medical outcomes.[215] Clinically, touch has been linked to reduced anxiety levels.[216] Touch may also lead to decreased heart rate, blood pressure and cortisol (a stress hormone) along with increased oxytocin (the hormone released which makes people feel good when they cuddle).[217]

Given the numerous beneficial effects of caring human touch, it is no wonder that some hospitals and hospices welcome "reiki things." They do not know there is a difference between an application of "reiki" where the practitioner gently touches and an application of Real Reiki® where the practitioner gently touches. In the first instance, the recipient gets the benefits of human touch. In the second, the recipient gets the same benefits and additionally gets the powerful benefit of a universal energy science which brings Radiant, whole energy to their entire body-mind-spirit dynamic.

Without something like a "universal energy metric," we have no overt tools for differentiating human touch using Real Reiki® from human touch which has no universal energy science connection. This is why what the technique is called can be so important. The use of the registered service marks which denote the intact transcendental science rediscovered by Dr. Usui, brought to the West by Hawayo Takata and passed to Dr. Barbara Ray, identify which application is being offered and provide a guarantee of receiving something more than simply a touch therapy.

It should be noted that this whole discussion, in relation to the history of Reiki, addresses the most basic application of Reiki: using the hands in specific positions on the head and body. There are other ways to apply the same universal, transcendental energy without the use of physical hands on or near a physical body. Mrs. Takata made it clear to students who wrote her that she had a mechanism to direct energy using the tools of Reiki, even when she was not there physically. However, these other degrees and the tools available with other degrees were part of her secrets. She gave all that information to Dr. Barbara Ray only to be shared after Mrs. Takata's death. Today, students of the Second Degree and beyond use some of these tools as part of their applications of the science.

Fortunately, with Real Reiki®, there is no need to believe or disbelieve: the formulas which are part of the intact science of Real Reiki® ensure that anyone who has been attuned by a properly-trained Authorized Instructor (teacher) has that access reliably and consistently for life. Neither the practitioner nor the recipient need to believe, concentrate, or do anything mentally to use or benefit from the energy. As Mrs. Takata said directly in 1939, "My patients do not have to believe in me or even concentrate while I am working on them."[218]

TRT®, Real Reiki®, can be used whether or not someone believes in it, and with babies, animals, food... the applications are unlimited. Additionally, with the Second Degree and beyond, practitioners can direct Radiant, whole energy using various methods for the recipient to use as their entire system needs it. Again, the practitioner does not need to decide – in fact, cannot decide – what the energy will do. The innate intelligence of a system with increased access to healing energy can use that energy for balance and greater wholeness.

14 REAL REIKI® AND PROFESSIONAL OUTREACH

In the decades since Mrs. Takata's death, the word "reiki" has become fairly well-known, even though most people do not have a clue what "reiki" is. However, since the word "reiki" itself is a generic term, it can (and does) mean anything someone wants to say about it.

Trademarks are a legal method of distinguishing and protecting specific, unique items. For example, for years the maker of Q-Tips® has posted the following notice on the home page of its website:

"Q-TIPS® is a registered trademark of Unilever and is NOT a name for just any cotton swabs. The Q-TIPS® trademark can only be used to refer to the specific cotton swab products manufactured and sold by Unilever and should not be used to refer to cotton swab products of other companies or to cotton swabs generally. Appropriate generic terminology for cotton swabs includes the terms 'cotton', 'stick(s)' and 'swab(s)'. Misuse of the Q-TIPS® trademark constitutes an infringement of Unilever's exclusive rights in the mark."[219]

The manufacturer of Kleenex® has tried to maintain

"Kleenex" as a unique trademark with "tissue" referring to any brand of paper tissues. However, in many regions, Kleenex® is a common term used generically, and at some point, without continuing protective efforts, the Kimberly-Clark company could lose that trademark.

"Service mark" is the term for a trademark of something non-material. Only Mrs. Takata could have registered the word "reiki" as a service mark, since she had been the authority on Reiki for decades. In 1980, she had already told many, many students to use the word, but she could still have proven prior and repeated use. However, she became ill and had to cancel the appointment scheduled with an attorney in April. She did not understand the situation's urgency enough to go to an attorney with Dr. Ray in August. Once Mrs. Takata died, the word "reiki" became meaningless, a word which can be used by anyone for anything they want... and that is what has happened.

For several years, the A.R.A. attempted to educate the public about the difference between anything called "reiki" and what was Mrs. Takata's Reiki. The organization's logo had been registered soon after A.R.A.'s founding and helped signal the intact system. As early as the first edition of *The Official Reiki Handbook* in 1982 – when the A.R.A. had expanded into the American-International Reiki Association (A.I.R.A.) – it was already necessary to include the following statement:

> "Before *investing* in a Reiki Seminar and in advanced Reiki degrees *be sure* that the instructor is a fully certified Reiki Master/Teacher endorsed by the American-International Reiki Association. Unfortunately, since the precise Reiki keys can and have been altered, changed and partially transmitted by others, the A.I.R.A. *endorses only* those Reiki Masters properly trained through its agency and *certifies* that the keys are unaltered and intact."[220]

Real Reiki® was registered as a service mark soon

thereafter. In 1987 the term "The Radiance Technique" was registered as an English-language phrase denoting the science, and the name of the A.I.R.A. is now The Radiance Technique International Association (TRTIA). Over the years, other phrases have been registered in English and other languages to provide a range of descriptors for Authorized Instructors and students. Every service mark held by TRTIA differentiates the complete, unaltered science of Reiki, Real Reiki®, from the many things called "reiki." Again, once the A.I.R.A. began registering service marks to help denote the intact science to the public, a variety of "reiki" practitioners copied the process, registering their own marks for their understanding of whatever they did. There are now more than two hundred trademarks or service marks which include the word "reiki" in the United States trademark database alone.[221] Some people also add identifiers like "Western Reiki" or "Reiki (Takata)," and again, this means nothing in terms of a guarantee.

No matter what words are used, only the service marks for the intact science assure a student they are learning the real thing. Today each and every Authorized Instructor of TRT®, Real Reiki® maintains a license to use the TRTIA service marks worldwide. Those specific service marks act as a guarantee that you will learn the intact, unaltered science as taught by Hawayo Takata to Dr. Barbara Ray, giving you direct access to universal, whole, harmless energy *for life.*

The classes have also grown and developed over the years. Mrs. Takata usually taught her First Degree classes in four two-hour evenings. This gave students the chance to come after work and after dinner. Mrs. Takata usually charged $150 for those eight hours. In 1937, right after Dr. Hayashi left Hawaii, Mrs. Takata also offered classes free to people over seventy.[222] However, she was adamant her whole life that students needed to pay for what they learned. She was trained by Dr. Hayashi that only those who were invested in their healing would get the most out of it. Some of the fees she set arose from this training. For example, that $150 fee in 1970 would be equivalent to $992 in 2019 dollars.[223] She told Dr. Ray that when she decided on a price for prospective Reiki Masters, she chose an amount equivalent at the time to a small house, thinking that would be a deterrent to all but the most dedicated of students.[224] As it turned out, there were a lot of people in the 1970's spending more than she imagined on these intriguing Eastern techniques.

Authorized Instructors now teach professional seminars around the world. The education offered in the seminars has expanded from those early eight-hour classes, too, with the First Degree presented in at least twelve hours over at least three days. All seven degrees are available in professional seminars to students if they choose to study through the Advanced Degrees. The Code of Ethics mentioned in Dr. Ray's first letter to all Reiki Masters has acted as an additional assurance of professionalism and quality.[225] While Authorized Instructors each have their own personal style and specialties, every one teaches the same material with the same high standards and ethics. In rare cases, the certifying body has had to discontinue certification when someone has repeatedly and egregiously violated the Ethical Principles,[226] another protection and guarantee for the public.

Mrs. Takata began the first draft of a Reiki handbook in 1948, but she really did not want students to write notes. Students were expected to pay attention and remember everything without writing it down. The first written material Dr. Ray created for American students was *The Official Reiki Handbook*, with chapters about Reiki, pictures of the basic hands-on positions, and a broad overview of anatomy and conditions in relation to using Real Reiki®. That book, now in its fourth edition, is given to every First Degree student as a resource for students of *all* degrees. Again, the list of conditions expanded into a separate book, now *The New Expanded Reference Manual of The Radiance Technique®, Authentic Reiki®* in its third edition, which is also included with classes.

Everything Dr. Barbara Ray suggested in the February 1981 letter from the A.R.A. has become a reality. As Mrs. Takata wanted, Reiki – Real Reiki®, TRT®, the Reiki which Mrs. Takata kept safe throughout her lifetime – is available for many, many people, presented in professional seminars worldwide.

15 REAL REIKI® AROUND THE WORLD

When Mrs. Takata passed Dr. Barbara Ray the Keys to Reiki, she had spent almost a decade actively looking for the right person. She also had some parameters for the person who would hold the keys safe for the next generation. First, Dr. Ray could not speak about the keys or the entirety of the science until after Mrs. Takata's death. Second, Mrs. Takata wanted to make Reiki available for everyone. She said to Dr. Ray, "You can say things I cannot because your eyes are not like this"... and she pointed at her slanted Japanese eyes.

Dr. Ray could have done anything with the keys. Mrs. Takata had maintained an exclusive personal fiefdom around Reiki for forty-five years. Dr. Ray could easily have continued in that tradition, keeping it as her personal technique and teaching only people she chose. There was certainly ample interest from Mrs. Takata's contacts around the United States and Canada. Instead, Dr. Ray embarked upon the very challenging path of creating a not-for-profit organization to act as the non-personal entity protecting and preserving Reiki, Real Reiki®, for her lifetime and beyond. Her vision of the American Reiki Association was of an organization which would serve *all* students, whether they were teachers or not. It would be the centerpoint of standards and ethical guidelines, make sure the educational materials were consistent, and would act overall for the support of all students of Real Reiki®, beyond the limitations of a single individual's situation or opinions. The Purposes (reprinted in Appendix C) of what is now called The Radiance Technique International Association are an amazing and unique formulation, in words, of higher principles and purposes.

Forming the A.R.A. was truly revolutionary. Through the centuries, schools which taught esoteric systems like Reiki were usually run by a single master teacher. When that master teacher died, often the school would, too, being succeeded by a different master teacher with his own group of students and own set of lessons. Some schools (like Dr. Hayashi's) were limited to students of a certain level and to elite students who would live with or near the master, not including everyone from every level and every background.

Within the first years of the A.R.A. – which soon became the American-International Reiki Association with increased international outreach – Dr. Ray created the basis of a body of knowledge about Real Reiki®. *The Official Handbook* was available in early 1982; *The Reiki Factor* in January 1983; the current Energy Model in 1984; the regular newsletters and journals from the association began in Spring 1981. The list of conditions originally in the Handbook became its own book, *The Expanded Reference Manual of The Radiance Technique®*, in 1987. All of these were tangible, written materials which supported students in the basic information and understanding about Real Reiki® and gave them more to support their growth as they continued their study of TRT®. With the availability of written materials, students were also not limited to what they remembered from class or what they thought made sense based on limited experience or other kinds of things they knew.

Dr. Ray took careful steps to ensure this nonprofit matured beyond a one-person operation. From its inception, the A.R.A. had a Board of Directors, staff members, and the correct outer form of a nonprofit corporation. In 1987, Dr. Ray moved into the position of Honorary Advisor to the Board, stepping away from any day-to-day operations as she herself did her own work.

Dr. Barbara Ray (c. 1988)

A large proportion of nonprofits fail within five years; others go out of business when their founders no longer run the corporation. Dr. Ray created a strong, flexible structure for this nonprofit, and a wealth of dedicated students have helped keep the organization moving and growing over the years. Thanks to the succession of people who have helped run TRTIA through the years, 2020 marks TRTIA's fortieth birthday, an enormous milestone for a small nonprofit.

From the beginning the A.I.R.A. developed a variety of projects and events to support students in their ongoing journey and discovery with the science. In April 1983 in

Atlanta, the A.I.R.A. presented the first international A.I.R.A. Reiki Conference, called "Dimensions of Healing and Wholeness." The keynote speaker was noted author and speaker Elisabeth Kübler-Ross, with eleven other speakers rounding out the weekend. The conference included music, stretching and yoga, and a bookstore.[227] Since that first conference, the A.I.R.A., now TRTIA, has held numerous conferences and gatherings for *all* students – not limited to teachers – with lively programs, stores full of books and interesting merchandise, and a diverse mix of speakers, facilitators, musicians, and experts in a wide range of supportive outer-plane practices. The second international conference was "Celebrating Transformation" in 1985 at Walt Disney World in Florida. Since then, conferences have been offered in different locations approximately every other year, with facilitators and participants from many countries. Again, Dr. Ray's vision was to encourage and nurture the expansion of every student, whether they became Authorized Instructors or not. These conferences have been one aspect fulfilling that vision.

Real Reiki® quickly became popular outside the United States, too. Mrs. Takata had always had invitations from Europe, but she said there was already too much work to do in the U.S.[228] Early on, Dr. Ray also offered lectures and classes in England. Throughout the 1980's, Dr. Ray traveled and taught thousands of students from different countries. A number of well-trained Authorized Instructors also traveled wherever there was interest, expanding Real Reiki® from its core of students in North America to Europe, South America and Australia. The first translation of the body of knowledge appeared in Germany in 1986, in an early version of *The Official Handbook*. Throughout the years TRTIA has overseen careful translations of the Handbook and *The 'Reiki' Factor in The Radiance Technique*® into several languages, with in-depth dialogues to bring the best possible versions of the source material to students with each edition. In 2011, *The Expanded Reference Manual* became a much larger book as *The New Expanded Reference Manual of The Radiance Technique®, Authentic Reiki®* (third edition). In recent years, TRTIA has brought both that new Manual and *The 'Reiki' Factor in The Radiance Technique®* into ebook format.

TRTIA has also coordinated expansive tours of destinations as varied as Egypt, the American Southwest and Alaska. Each event offers all students, to whatever degree of the science they have chosen to study, the opportunity to use the transcendental science of TRT® in many different ways and share experiences with other students.

In December 1983, what was then the A.I.R.A. began one project which may be the longest-running Light networking on the planet. As announced in *The Reiki Review*, all students who had the tools to direct energy were invited to join in at noon each day, the time of the most outer light where each person is, to direct to "Trusting and Loving Our Life's Unfolding Process."²²⁹ By 1985 this Noon Network had become a regular project for students of all Degrees to help the planet and all on it: "Since December 1983, we have been involved in an ongoing networking project to help planet Earth and to serve humanity by collectively and consciously directing the Reiki light-universal energy to generate peace, harmony and will-to-good."²³⁰ Today, TRT® students of all Degrees participate in the High Noon Network every day in every time zone.

Another planet-wide project began on November 1, 1997, when the very first online page for the Healing/Wholing Network was posted on the TRTIA website. People from everywhere – regardless of whether they have studied Authentic Reiki® or not – submit requests for Radiant support. Every day those requests are posted at the top of the page, so there is a list of people, places and situations for students to direct Radiant energy specifically to using the tools they learned in seminars. As described in *The Radiance Technique Journal,*

"Without knowing the people listed, without being part of their personal circle of friends, alumni of

The Radiance Technique®, Authentic Reiki® can provide *Real Radiant Support* for whatever processes are unfolding. As well as requests for support for individuals, the Healing/Wholing Network includes requests for energy to be directed to animals and to situations, natural disasters such as the recent Hurricane Georges, plane crashes, elections in various countries, and all the aspects of life and Being on this planet and beyond. Using TRT®, we are creating an inner-connected network of Radiant Supporters even though we may never meet on the outer planes."[231]

No matter where someone lives in the world, they are an integral part of this community of TRT® students.

There are many other programs offered by TRTIA which help fulfill TRTIA's purposes. For example, TRTIA collects experiential data from a very wide range of students for the archives. In some cases, that data comes from special service projects, where TRTIA funds Authorized Instructors who want to do projects such as teaching First Degree at no cost to home healthcare aides, hospice volunteers, single mothers, women over 75, school counselors, and other groups. Thousands of books about The Radiance Technique®, Real Reiki® have also been donated to doctors, veterinarians, libraries, schools and more.

In more recent years, TRTIA has reached out worldwide via emails, online meetings and an app. There are weekly tips for students about using The Radiance Technique® and online meetings to explore topics of interest and spend time using TRT® together in a unified field of Radiant energy. Service mark license holders have opportunities to participate in continuing education and TRTIA continues to protect and defend the service marks which denote and distinguish the intact science.

Dr. Barbara Ray has anchored a light-based organization in outer form on this planet, providing "Radiant Service to the public." The very first TRTIA Purpose is to "protect and

130

preserve The Radiance Technique® (TRT®), Authentic Reiki®, Real Reiki®, a complete intact Science of Universal, Radiant, Light energy, for present and future generations in perpetuity in global consciousness, harmony, healing/wholing and unconditional love."[232] That alone is a lifetime's work, and points to the potential of what can be done with Real Reiki®, The Radiance Technique® by those who choose to dedicate themselves to it.

The historical thread seems so unlikely: a Japanese naval officer to a Japanese-American woman from Hawaii to a university professor in Georgia, each one a holder of the Keys to Reiki for their generation. Mrs. Takata did not have the background or education to separate the science of Reiki itself from the confines of her cultural boundaries. In her passing the keys to Dr. Barbara Ray, she asked Dr. Ray to broaden the audience for Real Reiki®. Through more than four decades, Dr. Ray has indeed fulfilled her promise to Hawayo Takata. She has dedicated her life to Real Reiki®, and provided the tools for Real Reiki®, The Radiance Technique®, TRT® to be available for current and future generations. Thanks to both Mrs. Takata's and Dr. Ray's lifelong efforts to protect and preserve an intact, ancient science of energy, hundreds of thousands of students around the world have had the amazing, expansive and profound opportunity to use Real Reiki®, TRT® in their own lives.

APPENDIX A
HISTORICAL PERSPECTIVES ON
THE RADIANCE TECHNIQUE®, AUTHENTIC REIKI®
by Dr. Barbara Ray

From 1978 - 1980, I had the honor of studying Reiki extensively with Hawayo Takata in her private home in Iowa. In the following article, I have written about some of the aspects of the profound relationship that existed between Takata and myself, and the depth of her Purpose in protecting the Intact Keys to the precious treasure known to her as Reiki, Usui Shiki Ryoho, as the Reiki Method of Natural Healing, as the Usui System and as the Usui System of Reiki Healing.

During these extended times with Takata, she instructed me in the entire, intact Seven Degrees of the Usui System of Natural Healing, Reiki, and passed the complete Keys to me. As taught by Takata, Hyashi and Usui, the only way to activate and transmit Reiki is through the correct, intact and non-polluted Keys. **Please note** *also that the Usui 'Reiki' Keys have never been passed according to lineage which is defined as one's ancestors and family. The process has, in fact, been one of succession defined as a process of following in order. In this sequence, Dr. Jujiro Hyashi was Dr. Mikao Usui's successor, Takata was Dr. Hyashi's successor and Dr. Barbara Ray is Takata's successor.*

Please note, Takata did not register any of these names (Reiki, Usui Shiki Ryoho, the Reiki Method of Natural Healing, etc.), and she granted to those she instructed the rights to use all these 'Reiki' names. Through many decades, the widespread use of these terms has put them into the public domain.

The term "rei-ki"

In considering the evolution of The Radiance Technique®, Authentic Reiki®, you find that the term rei-ki is actually two distinct Japanese words combined to denote the cosmic energy science rediscovered in ancient texts by Dr. Mikao Usui. Please note that there is no actual proof, just legend, that Dr. Usui called this science "reiki". He predated Mrs. Hawayo Takata by many decades. However, "reiki" is the term used by Mrs. Takata and she explained to me that *rei* refers to Cosmic, Universal energy and *ki* refers to the life energy of the physical, outer bodies (the three outer planes). By joining these two words the term *reiki* conveyed the concept of the energy of "The Whole" and the aligning of the part (ki) with Whole, Cosmic, Universal (rei) in an ever-expanding principle of dynamic interaction and evolution.

In 1983, I published the *first-ever* book on this science of Transcendental energy, *The Reiki Factor*. In that book, "reiki" was used as a verb, as an adjective and as a noun, as the name of the science and as referring to the uses of this technique as well. However, since that time, the word "reiki" has been used in such generalized, vague and incorrect ways that by necessity in order to protect and denote **the authentic**, intact science and technique new terms are now used and have been registered in many countries. Simply a generic term, "reiki" can be used by anyone for *anything*. Since it had been widely used as a generic term, it was not possible to register it... that would have had to have been done by Takata many years ago. The Radiant power of this science is accessed and transmitted through its inner-connected system of universal symbols and Attunement Processes, *not* by saying the word "reiki" or any word at all. The Radiance Technique®, Authentic Reiki®, Real Reiki®, The Official Reiki Program® and TRT® are the main terms registered now in the necessity of denoting and distinguishing, from "whatever reiki things," the intact and complete Cosmic energy science rediscovered by Dr. Usui. The entire system was passed *intact* from Usui to Hyashi to Takata and, then, to me in 1979. Since that time, the use of this technique, *now* known as The Radiance Technique®, Authentic Reiki®, has grown and spread into a world-wide outreach encircling the globe.

About "the reiki factor"

Now, in *this* book [*The Authentic Reiki*® *(Das Authentische Reiki), Der ,Reiki' Faktor in Der Radiance Technik*® by Dr. Barbara Ray, translated into German by Margarete Keppel and Ulrike Wolf, 1995] I have used the phrase 'the Reiki factor' using the word "Reiki" not to denote the system itself, since that is no longer possible due its widespread misuse but in a phrase referring to the *factor,* the *component* of Radiant, Transcendental, Pure Light energy which *is the Inner Essence* of this science. 'The Reiki Factor' – that is, the factor of the vibration of Radiant, Transcendental Light – *is that which is accessed directly* by means of the unique interacting from the interior of the component parts functioning *within* this system. The complete science is written in the *language* of Universal Symbols which transmit through *vibration* "knowledge" of the Transcendental Planes. The various Attunement Processes within this energy science are composed of these Symbols, which themselves *vibrate* aspects of wholeness. All of these parts are formed from *within* the interior of the Whole, and, the interior of the Whole is greater than the sum of the individual parts. Every aspect of this science is inner-connected/interconnected to the *whole, intact system.* The inner parts derive their special functions from the whole, *not* from other parts. Each of the Seven Degrees of The Radiance Technique®, Authentic Reiki® is a subsystem within a Whole. When any of the parts are used as separate from the inner-connection to the Whole system, then *whatever that is* becomes a mere imitation devoid of the capacity to access directly Radiant, Transcendental energy which is the *inherent* purpose of this system rediscovered by Usui. When you receive the *intact* Attunements, Transcendental energy within you is *activated* and when you use this technique, you are bringing this 'Reiki factor' into your daily life at any time – in any place. 'The Reiki Factor' *is* Universal, Radiant Light energy which is *inherently* harmless, benevolent and *always* spirals in the direction of wholing/healing on all planes of Being responding to the unique, inner needs of each individual.

After Takata's death in 1980

Since Mrs. Takata's death in 1980, extensive fragmentation, misrepresentation, confusion in thinking and lack of correct information and knowledge have occurred concerning the polluted, disconnected and partial "something called reiki" which is *not at all* the actual intact science that was rediscovered and passed on by Dr. Usui. Individuals who do not have access to the whole system and who do not even have *knowledge* of the correct Attunement Processes have been randomly "making teachers and so-called reiki masters." Using parts disconnected from the whole, intact system and inventing formulas and methods which were *never* related to the correct process of activating and accessing Universal energy within this system is a misguided, unfounded, irresponsible practice having *no relation or connection whatever to the system rediscovered by Dr. Usui,* no matter what it is called. Whatever that "something" is, it is sometimes referred to as "reiki," often with other descriptive words added and is peddled by individuals who know *nothing* of this incredible Cosmic science The Radiance Technique®, Authentic Reiki® Takata received from Hyashi, who received from Usui, the whole, not parts, intact Keys to this Cosmic science of Radiant, Universal energy. There are no other versions of the *original Reiki* and there was no split thereby creating other groups... that simply is not possible. Dr. Usui's, Dr. Hyashi's, Mrs. Takata's and Dr. Ray's Keys are *one and the same: the original, intact, authentic Reiki : anything else is an imitation, a copy, a part and a fabrication.* These so-called "reiki things" are parts and fragments and parts are *not the whole.* Indeed these very references themselves are *completely dishonoring* to the integrity of Dr. Usui's passing of the Real, Intact Keys.

For nearly half of her eighty years, Mrs. Takata held her complete knowledge of this Cosmic Science from public view protecting it in purposeful secretiveness and silence. One must comprehend the world situation and realize that she lived a large portion of her adult life during one of the most difficult, trying and devastating periods of American *and* World history in the years prior to, during and following World War II. Due to the unusual context and stressful circumstances of her life, she found herself to be *the living* protector of this Universal energy science in an environment which made it necessary to keep secret and silent about it. She lived during a highly intense time of East-West polarities and *both* by her nature and her Japanese/Eastern heritage *and* by the prevailing winds of discord, hostilities and prejudices surrounding her *entire* life, she was firm in her resolve and commitment to holding her knowledge of this Cosmic science in privacy, in silence and in non-public display.

Personal, direct knowledge from Hawayo Takata

What I know about Hawayo Takata is *first-hand, direct* knowledge from *her.* During the last several years of her life, I had both the honor and the privilege of being with her in the privacy of her own home, in a small town in Iowa, for *many* weeks of intense study and training. In addition, in August, 1980, I had the special honor of having her as a guest and teacher in my home in Atlanta for more than a month. During those private times, she intimately told me the story of her entire life and revealed the depth of her own personal trials and struggles as an uneducated woman widowed early in her adult life and as the main support of a young family. Much of what she told me was very personal and very private and will remain with me as such. From *the very moment* we *first* looked into each other's eyes, a deep and abiding special bond between us existed. This instant Heart bond sparked between us in that moment in time and has ever since and *always* been our Forever connection. This Radiant Love connection radiated from within encircling us in a Silent and Knowing Trust. And, it was within this intense and enlightening Radiance that she revealed the entire science, that she initiated me to all levels and thoroughly instructed me and passed the complete Keys of the intact, whole system. She called this Transcendental energy science "Reiki" and claimed it was passed with this name to her from Dr. Hyashi. Remember, she never knew Dr. Usui and there could be as much as nearly a century separating them.

In tracing the recent history of this energy science, you must realize that Takata received all the Keys, whole and intact, in the late 1930's from Hyashi in Japan. She was *not* a member of his family, *nor* was she a native of Japan, *nor* was she highly educated, and she was a female and claimed to be the *first* woman ever to receive the complete Keys to the Seven Degrees of the authentic, Usui system. She was the *only* person in the West who could initiate anyone into any Degree of this Cosmic Science until the early or mid-1970's. Born in 1900, her age was also early to mid-'70's. In the few years prior to her death, she did allow a few people to teach The First Degree. However, true to her tradition of maintaining silence and protection, she did not disclose the details of the entire Usui system to anyone else, until my studies with her. Most often when she taught someone The First Degree, she did not mention that there was a Second Degree. In addition, from the very beginning of her training and teachings with me, she requested that, while she was living, I not discuss or print anything regarding the entire system, and that I not initiate any teachers. I always honored her requests and honored *her* as the Authority and Master Initiator.

Hawayo Takata
passing the intact keys to Dr. Barbara Ray

Sixteen years [*Ed.: original article written and published in 1995*] have now gone by since Takata's death in 1980! She had passed to me the Keys to this Transcendental, Cosmic energy science in its *entirety* in order to keep the *continuity* of making this precious science available in a new cycle and in a new context and to continue to protect, maintain and preserve this unique science *whole* and *intact*. During these years, I have been so doing. She and I had begun planning for an Association which was founded in 1980... she was present in Atlanta at the first-ever public meeting of The Reiki Association as its first and greatly honored guest. She spoke to the whole group and then spent much time graciously meeting personally with nearly all the two hundred people attending. That association continues today known as The Radiance Technique International Association, Inc. (TRTIA). Also, she spent many days both at The Reiki Center, which I had opened in 1978, and at my home meeting more people and training two others to become teachers. She and I had begun the long process of providing for the need to train and authorize persons to teach this Cosmic science in future years and such training continues with ongoing improvements.

I inherited from Takata this Universal energy science in a context and world quite different from what hers had been; likewise, hers had been very different from Hyashi's or Usui's. Each of us holding these Keys has a role in a cycle different from the preceding ones yet we are profoundly and forever connected. Each of us and those to follow is first and foremost the protector, the guardian of this intact science. Each of us must accept the responsibility to maintain this science, whole and intact, and, each of us has to struggle with many difficult issues involved in making this Cosmic energy science available and in maintaining *integrity* around it. Some of the main parts of my role so far have been in training others to teach, in identifying this Transcendental energy science and its link to other such sciences known on this planet from ancient times, in writing about this energy science, in lecturing and teaching in many countries to varied groups as well as privately to individuals. In addition, the gateway for the opportunity for more people to study the TRT® First and Second Degree has been greatly expanded in these sixteen years and will continue to so do. Likewise, the gateway for the opportunity for studying all Seven of the TRT® Degrees has been opened beginning another cycle. Of course there are many difficulties, many unknowns, and many complex considerations in this unfolding and expanding process involving this science requiring much time for thoughts, for reflections and, most of all, for meditations... there are no easy, quick or superficial answers... there was no "how to" book passed, just the Keys... there are things that sometimes work and things that do not. It is an ongoing dedication to experiment and learning from what has been done and knowing when to let go and when and how to begin again... there is simply *no way* for me or for anyone to satisfy *all* the needs, demands and suggestions of everyone and there is no way "to do it all" everywhere in every country at this time in any *one* lifetime! Indeed, there are now and there will be others to help carry on in the years to come and to ensure the ongoing continuity and integrity of The Radiance Technique®, Authentic Reiki® in the Third Millennium.

The information
about this science is correct and protected
In stabilizing and in expanding The Radiance Technique® in any country, it is paramount to the endeavor to distribute correct information regarding this science, to speak and to write about it correctly and to train others properly and diligently to transmit and teach about this Cosmic energy science...taking one step at a time to ensure that the foundation is steady and strong. This reminds me of the Ancient Chinese proverb "A Journey of a thousand miles

begins with the first step." So, likewise, it can be said that The Journey of The Radiance Technique®, Authentic Reiki® into a thousand centuries begins with the first step.

Likewise, its process of becoming available in many countries to many people represents a series of deeply significant and meaningful steps in the journey to steadiness, availability and protection of the intactness and wholeness of this Universal energy science throughout the next decades and centuries. In addition, as a unifying factor, "TRT" to designate The Radiance Technique® has been service marked and registered in many countries so that, in *any* language, it can become *known* to stand for the intact, complete, original, genuine and legitimate The Radiance Technique®, Authentic Reiki®, Real Reiki® discovered by Dr. Usui and passed to Dr. Hyashi, then to Mrs. Takata and from her, directly and in living person, to me.

Original copyright © 1995 Dr. Barbara Ray

Reprinted with permission from The New Expanded Reference Manual of The Radiance Technique®, Authentic Reiki®. Third ed. Dr. Barbara Ray. St. Petersburg, FL: Radiance Associates, 2013.

Appendix B
Service Marks of
The Radiance Technique
International Association, Inc.

The logo above and the following are registered service marks of The Radiance Technique International Association, Inc. (TRTIA) and phrases used to identify the authentic, intact and complete system of The Radiance Technique®, Authentic Reiki®, Real Reiki®. They are used for this purpose by TRTIA and by Radiance Seminars, Inc. and Authorized Instructors under license. Authorized Instructors use the following phrases to identify the seminars they teach for The First Degree or The Second Degree Official Program of The Radiance Technique®, Authentic Reiki®. Make sure to look for them when planning to take a seminar.

> The Radiance Technique®
> The First Degree Official Program of
>   The Radiance Technique®
> The Second Degree Official Program of
>   The Radiance Technique®
> The Third Degree Official Program of
>   The Radiance Technique®
> TRT®
> Radiant Touch®
> Authentic Reiki®

Real Reiki®
The Official Reiki Program®
The Intact Master Keys of The Radiance Technique®
The Radiant TRT Heart First Ashram®

The registered service marks of The Radiance Technique International Association, Inc. (TRTIA, formerly A.I.R.A.), denote and distinguish the real, complete, intact science from things called "reiki." Only those contractually and legally authorized may use the TRTIA service marks. TRTIA has also registered and holds service marks denoting this intact science in various regions and countries around the world. For further information, contact TRTIA.

Appendix C
Purposes of The Radiance Technique International Association, Inc.

1. To protect and preserve the complete intact Science of Universal, Radiant, Light energy known as The Radiance Technique® (TRT®), Authentic Reiki®, Real Reiki®, for present and future generations in perpetuity in global consciousness, harmony, healing/wholing and unconditional love;

2. To promote, protect, enhance and expand the public understanding of and interest in The Radiance Technique® by providing a non-voting international membership for both alumni of The Radiance Technique®, TRT®, Authentic Reiki® and other interested supporters; and to establish, support and encourage the ongoing expansion of The Radiant TRT Heart First Ashram® on an international basis;

3. To provide for research and development projects and publishing projects pertaining to The Radiance Technique®, Real Reiki®, and to promote through education, research and distribution of materials the widespread understanding of the science of universal energy, which is helpful, beneficent and benevolent to All Peoples in the basic human right to achieve wholeness, balance, health in body, mind and spirit; peace, integrity, intelligence, love, spiritual awakening and enlightenment;

4. To explore and record the interaction of The Radiance Technique® (TRT®), Authentic Reiki®, with the living dynamic of people in their daily lives, with plants and animals and with all other living systems; to maintain experiential data from the alumni of The Radiance Technique® (TRT®), Real Reiki®, and the use of Radiant Touch® as social research and service for this and future generations; and to maintain an accurate historical recording of the history of The

Radiance Technique® (TRT®) as a permanent archive and to provide and protect the continuance of TRT® archives;

5. To provide for the ongoing education of the public regarding The Radiance Technique®, Radiant Touch®, Real Reiki®, and to publish materials on a continuous basis as a service to members as well as distribute publications as part of varied educational projects; and to support the worldwide outreach of information through preparation and distribution of materials concerning The Radiance Technique® (TRT®), Authentic Reiki®, in written, audio/visual and electronic forms; and to establish and maintain endowments to support the printing and distribution of materials about The Radiance Technique®, Real Reiki®;

6. To aid in Service to All Life Forms through the understanding of the Essential Unity and Oneness of All Life and the Essential Peaceful Inner-Relationship of the Transcendental, Universal Energy Principle inherent in All Life;

7. To promote international understanding and cooperation in responsible group service for humanity and all life, in mutual respect, love and harmlessness, in peaceful caretaking and in the principle of unity within our diversities; to be a center for and to cooperate with other organizations in benevolent activities contributing to global stability, unity, peace, and the continuing development of right human relations and the evolution of expanded consciousness for all of humanity's unfolding process; to contribute to increasing in knowledge and understanding of the dignity and worth of all human beings, of all animals and of all living things, and to promote right human relations and peaceful co-existence among all peoples and all living things on planet Earth.

APPENDIX D
BOOKS & MATERIALS ABOUT REAL REIKI®

- ❖ Dr. Barbara Ray, *The 'Reiki' Factor in The Radiance Technique®, Expanded Edition* (print and ebook editions)
- ❖ Dr. Barbara Ray, *The New Expanded Reference Manual of The Radiance Technique®, Authentic Reiki® (Third Edition)*
- ❖ Dr. Barbara Ray, *The Radiance Technique®, Authentic Reiki® — Managing Stress*
- ❖ Dr. Barbara Ray, *The Authentic Reiki® (Das Authentische Reiki®), Der ,Reiki' Faktor in Der Radiance Technik®, Das authentische Reiki®* (German translation by Margarete Keppel and Ulrike Wolf)
- ❖ Shoshana Shay, *Reiki History: Real Reiki® from Japan to the Western World*
- ❖ Katherine Lenel, *The Radiance Technique® and Cancer*
- ❖ Van Ault, *The Radiance Technique® and AIDS*
- ❖ Yesnie Carrington, *The Radiance Technique®, Authentic Reiki®, Empowerment and Wellbeing Strategies with Surgery and Related Experiences*
- ❖ Christine Gross, *We Are Timeless: The Radiance Technique® in Hospice Care*
- ❖ Ulrike Wolf, *Die Radiance Technik®, Das authentische Reiki®*
- ❖ Marvelle Lightfields, *The Radiance Technique® and The Animal Kingdom*
- ❖ Fred W. Wright, Jr., *The Radiance Technique® on the Job, Expanded Edition*
- ❖ Van Ault, *Hypnotherapy and The Radiance Technique®* (book and video)
- ❖ Anne Keltie, *The Radiance Technique® and Death and Dying*
- ❖ *Did You Know? Volume I* (desktop flipbook)
- ❖ *Did You Know? Volume II* (desktop flipbook)
- ❖ *TRT® Practice Cards* (box set of 200)

Appendix E
For Further Information

The Radiance Technique International Association, Inc.
(TRTIA)
P.O. Box 40570
St. Petersburg, FL 33743-0570
Email: TRTIA@trtia.org
Web: www.trtia.org
Online Store: www.trtiastore.org
App: www.trtia.info
Books about The Radiance Technique®, Real Reiki®; e-newsletters; regional TRT® resources; continuing education for TRT® students; experiential data archives; service mark usage.

Radiance Seminars, Inc. (RSI)
1275 66th St. N., #47727
St. Petersburg, FL 33743-7727
Email: RSISeminars@gmail.com
Web: www.radianceseminars.net
Seminars for The Third through The Seventh Degrees of The Radiance Technique®, Authentic Reiki®, including The Official Teacher Training program.

Book website: www.reikihistory.com

ABOUT THE AUTHOR

Shoshana Shay studied music and history at Bryn Mawr College, graduating cum laude with Highest Honors in Music. While pursuing her career as a classical and opera singer, she studied the First Degree of what was then simply called Reiki. In 1986, she became an Authorized Instructor of Real Reiki®, and has continued her study of the science through the Seventh Degree. Shay is a member of the Teacher Training Faculty and authorized and assigned by Radiance Seminars, Inc. to teach the Advanced Degrees of The Radiance Technique®, Real Reiki®. She is the collector for the trilogy of books called 'This Moment in Time', The Awakening Journey® Day by Day, three volumes of selected teachings of Dr. Barbara Ray to use in a daily practice on the Heart First Journey®.

Shay is also a consultant in computer interfaces and stress management. She expresses her creativity in a variety of ways, including book design, e-book coding, information systems creation, and music-making of many kinds. Shay's earlier research publications were annotated editions of the collected songs of Bettine von Arnim and Clara Schumann as well as plainchant by Hildegard von Bingen.

ENDNOTES

1. U.S. Department of the Interior, "Pacific Island Network Vital Signs Monitoring Plan," National Park Service, last modified September 29, 2004, https://irma.nps.gov/DataStore/DownloadFile/575333.
2. Barbara Weber Ray, Ph.D. and Yesnie Carrington, *The Official Reiki Handbook* (St. Petersburg, FL: American- International Reiki Association, 1982), 2.
3. "Pagh," Memory Alpha, accessed June 15, 2019, https://memory-alpha.fandom.com/wiki/Pagh.
4. Hawayo Takata, Handwritten autobiography, ca. 1973, Hawayo Takata Papers. ARC Mss 86, Special Research Collections, UCSB Library, University of California, Santa Barbara, CA,16.
5. Sally Hammond, *We Are All Healers* (New York, NY: Harper & Row, 1973), 261.
6. Barbara Ray, Ph.D., *The Reiki Factor* (Smithtown, NY: Exposition Press, Inc., 1983), 5.
7. Barbara Ray, Ph.D., *The New Expanded Reference Manual of The Radiance Technique®, Authentic Reiki®*, third ed. (St. Petersburg, FL: Radiance Associates, 2013), 142.
8. "Mrs. Takata to Open Office," Hawaii Tribune-Herald (Hilo, TH), May 28, 1939.
9. "Hawayo Takata: Cash Receipts & Disbursements Statements," 1962, Hawayo Takata Papers. ARC Mss 86, Special Research Collections, UCSB Library, University of California, Santa Barbara, CA.
10. Takata, Handwritten autobiography (ca. 1973).
11. "Mrs. Takata to Open Office" (1939).
12. Hawayo Takata, Transcript of Dr. Usui story, August 24, 1980, The Radiance Technique International Association, Inc., St. Petersburg, FL, 1.
13 Maxine H. Sullivan to Nonie C. Greene, July 6, 1983, TRTIA Archives, The Radiance Technique International Association, Inc., St. Petersburg, FL.
14. Takata, Transcript of Dr. Usui story, 2.
15. Takata, Transcript of Dr. Usui story, 3.
16. Takata, Transcript of Dr. Usui story, 3-4.
17. Exposition Press, Smithtown, New York, first printing in January 1983; later updated in a new edition and re-titled *The 'Reiki' Factor in The Radiance Technique®* (1992).
18. Ray, *The Reiki Factor*, 45.
19. Takata, Transcript of Dr. Usui story, 8.
20. Eleanor C. Nordyke and Y. Scott Matsumoto, "Japanese in Hawaii: a Historical and Demographic Perspective," in *eVols* (Honolulu, HI:

Hawaiian Historical Society, n.d.), 162, previously published in *Hawaiian Journal of History* 11 (1977), accessed May 23, 2019, http://hdl.handle.net/10524/528.

21. Nordyke and Matsumoto, "Japanese in Hawaii," in *eVols*, 162.
22. Smithsonian Institution, "Hawaii - History and Heritage," Smithsonian.com, last modified November 6, 2007, https://www.smithsonianmag.com/travel/hawaii-history-and-heritage-4164590/.
23. Hawaii, Kingdom of. Bureau of Immigration. *Report of the President of the Bureau of Immigration to the Legislative Assembly of 1886.* (Honolulu, 1886), p. 58; quoted in Northdyke & Matsumoto, "Japanese in Hawaii," in *eVols*, 163.
24. "Japanese Immigration," *Planters' Monthly 7* (January 1888) as quoted in Harry N. Scheiber and Jane L. Scheiber, *Bayonets in Paradise: Martial Law in Hawai'i during World War II* (University of Hawai'i Press, 2016), 10, Kindle edition.
25. Northdyke & Matsumoto, "Japanese in Hawaii," in *eVols*, 163.
26. Hawayo Takata, Transcript of taped autobiography, December 1979, The Radiance Technique International Association, Inc., St. Petersburg, FL, 6.
27. In the 1910 census, he said he was 43, which makes his birth year approximately 1867. By the 1940 census he said he was 66, which would have put his birthdate about 1874. Travel records from the early part of the century all agree with a birth year of 1867 or 1868.
28. Kuykendall, Ralph S., *The Hawaiian Kingdom, 1854-1874* (Honolulu, Univ of Hawaii Press, 1966), p. 183, quoted in Northdyke & Matsumoto, "Japanese in Hawaii," in *eVols*, 163.
29. George F. Nellist, "Statewide County HI Archives Biographies..... Makee, James November 24, 1812 - September 16, 1879," in *USGenWeb Archives*, previously published as "The Story of Hawaii and Its Builders," *The Honolulu Star Bulletin* (Territory of Hawaii), 1925, accessed July 22, 2019, http://files.usgwarchives.net/hi/statewide/bios/makee49bs.txt.
30. Hank Soboleski, "Kauai's Spalding Monument," *The Garden Island* (Lihue, HI), April 29, 2018.
31. Peter T. Young, "Colonel Zephaniah Swift Spalding," Images of Old Hawai'i, last modified February 3, 2015, http://imagesofoldhawaii.com/colonel-zephaniah-swift-spalding/.
32. Special to The New York Times. "COL. Z. M. SPALDING, EX-NEW YORKER, DEAD." *New York Times (1923-Current file)*; Jun 21, 1927; ProQuest Historical Newspapers: The New York Times, 25.
33. "Makee Sugar Co.," *The Garden Island* (Lihue, TH), December 22, 1914, 12.

34. "Owns Land in Every Quarter of Globe," *The Garden Island* (Lihue, TH), November 19, 1912, 3.
35. William A. Russ, Jr., "The Role of Sugar in Hawaiian Annexation," *The Pacific Historical Review* XII, no. 4 (December 1943): 340.
36. Takata, Transcript of taped autobiography, 1.
37. Takata, Transcript of taped autobiography, 1.
38. Takata, Transcript of taped autobiography, 2.
39. Ernest K. Wakukawa, *A History of the Japanese People in Hawaii* (Honolulu, TH: The Tokyo Shoin, 1938), 403.
40. The following material is drawn primarily from the transcript of the many tapes she made in 1979: Hawayo Takata, Transcript of taped autobiography, December 1979, The Radiance Technique International Association, Inc., St. Petersburg, FL.
41. Takata, Transcript of taped autobiography, 2-4.
42. Coinnews Media Group, LLC, "Inflation Calculator," US Inflation Calculator, accessed August 11, 2019, https://www.usinflationcalculator.com.
43. Takata, Transcript of taped autobiography, 4.
44. Takata, Transcript of taped autobiography, 4.
45. Takata, Transcript of taped autobiography, 5.
46. "Married an Italian Nobleman," *Hawaiian Gazette* (Honolulu, TH), September 18, 1903, 4.
47. Takata, Transcript of taped autobiography, 5.
48. Takata, Transcript of taped autobiography, 5.
49. "Makee Sugar Co." (1914).
50. Dennis M. Ogawa and Glen Grant, *Kodomo No Tame Ni-For the Sake of the Children: The Japanese-American Experience in Hawaii* (Honolulu, HI: University of Hawaii Press, 1980), 53 et passim, Google.
51. "Japanese Buy Thrift Stamps," *The Garden Island* (Lihue, TH), March 12, 1918, 1; currency calculation from Coinnews Media Group, LLC, "Inflation Calculator," US Inflation Calculator.
52. "Legion Dance is Huge Success," *The Garden Island* (Lihue, TH), April 25, 1922, 2.
53. "Wailua Golf Club Holds First Tournament," *The Garden Island* (Lihue, TH), November 8, 1921.
54. "Some Favorite Local Recipes," *Honolulu Star-Bulletin* (Honolulu, TH), July 22, 1926.
55. "Reiki Slaw," *The Reiki Review* I, no. 1 (Spring 1981): 2.
56. "Col. Spalding is Paid Honor," *Honolulu Star-Bulletin* (Honolulu, TH), April 24, 1930.
57. Home, Maeda Hospital, https://www.maeda-hospital-tokyo.jp/.
58. Takata, Transcript of taped autobiography, 102.

59. Takata, Handwritten autobiography (ca. 1973), 18.
60. "Three Kauai Officials In," *Honolulu Star-Bulletin* (Honolulu, TH), January 7, 1931.
61. "Y.M.B.A. Party Sails Thursday," *Honolulu Star-Bulletin* (Honolulu, TH), July 13, 1932, 10.
62. Ogawa and Grant, *Kodomo No Tame*, 53 et passim.
63. Honpa Hongwanji Hawaii Betsuin, "Temple History," Honpa Hongwanji Hawaii Betsuin, accessed August 9, 2019, https://hawaiibetsuin.org/temple-history/.
64. Ogawa and Grant, *Kodomo No Tame*, 55.
65. Ogawa and Grant, *Kodomo No Tame*, 55.
66. Hilo Hongwanji Mission to Hawayo Takata, memorandum, "Resolution of Appreciation," December 11, 1961, Hawayo Takata papers. ARC Mss 86, Special Research Collections, UCSB Library, University of California, Santa Barbara, CA.
67. Dr. Barbara Ray, interview by the author, St. Petersburg, FL, August 4, 2012.
68. Hawayo Takata, Typewritten autobiography, ca. 1973, Hawayo Takata Papers. ARC Mss 86, Special Research Collections, UCSB Library, University of California, Santa Barbara, CA.
69. Takata, Transcript of taped autobiography, 6.
70. Ancestry.com, Passenger list, *M.S. Asama Maru*.
71. Takata, Transcript of taped autobiography, 7.
72. All direct quotes in this section come from Takata, Transcript of taped autobiography, 10-14.
73. Chujiro Hayashi to Hawayo Takata, memorandum, "(First Degree)," December 13, 1935, Hawayo Takata papers. ARC Mss 86, Special Research Collections, UCSB Library, University of California, Santa Barbara, CA.
74. Ancestry.com, Passenger lists.
75. Chujiro Hayashi to Hawayo Takata, memorandum, "(Third Degree)," October 1, 1936, Hawayo Takata papers. ARC Mss 86, Special Research Collections, UCSB Library, University of California, Santa Barbara, CA.
76. Takata, Transcript of taped autobiography, 19.
77. "Reiki Sanitarium Treatments," advertisement, *The Garden Island* (Lihue, TH), October 13, 1936.
78. Sanitarium, "Moments that made us: Our Story," Sanitarium, accessed August 14, 2019, https://www.sanitarium.co.nz/about/sanitarium-story/history.
79. Takata, Transcript of taped autobiography, 23.
80. Takata, Typewritten autobiography (ca. 1973).
81. Ancestry.com, Passenger list, *Chichibu Maru*.

82. Chujiro Hayashi to Hawayo Takata, memorandum, February 21, 1938, Private collection of Dr. Barbara Ray, St. Petersburg, FL.
83. Nakamura, Kelli Y. "Wilfred Tsukiyama." *Densho Encyclopedia.* Accessed August 9, 2019. http://encyclopedia.densho.org/Wilfred%20Tsukiyama/.
84. Takata, Transcript of taped autobiography, 30.
85. Takata, Transcript of taped autobiography, 18.
86. "Reception Honors Japanese Visitor," ca. 1937, Hawayo Takata Papers. ARC Mss 86, Special Research Collections, UCSB Library, University of California, Santa Barbara, CA.
87. "Mrs. Takata to Open Office" (1939).
88. *Hawaii Tribune-Herald* (Hilo, TH). "At Hilo Hotel." May 24, 1939 and subsequent ads.
89. *Hawaii Tribune-Herald* (Hilo, TH). "Misses Hirata, Martin Assist Mrs. Takata." August 27, 1939.
90. "Misses Hirata, Martin Assist Mrs. Takata" (1939).
91. *Hawaii Tribune-Herald* (Hilo, TH). "Reiki Treatments." November 13, 1939.
92. *Hawaii Tribune-Herald* (Hilo, TH). "Mrs. Takata and Daughters to Honolulu." August 30, 1939, 3.
93. *Honolulu Star-Bulletin* (Honolulu, TH). "Land Court Deeds." October 24, 1939, 10.
94. Wakukawa, *A History of the Japanese*, 411-412.
95. Ancestry.com, Passenger lists.
96. *Hawaii Tribune-Herald* (Hilo, TH). "Health Studio." Advertisement. December 7, 1940.
97. *Hawaii Tribune-Herald* (Hilo, TH). "Honors Mother." May 26, 1941.
98. For an eminently readable and evocative account, see Gavin Daws' classic *Shoal of Time*, now reprinted in a fiftieth-anniversary edition and e-book.
99. Harry N. Scheiber and Jane L. Scheiber, *Bayonets in Paradise: Martial Law in Hawai'i during World War II* (University of Hawai'i Press, 2016), 41, Kindle edition.
100. Nordyke and Matsumoto, "Japanese in Hawaii," in *eVols*, 165-166.
101. Takata, Transcript of taped autobiography, 62.
102. Takata, Transcript of taped autobiography, 43-44.
103. Takata, Transcript of taped autobiography, 44.
104. Takata, Transcript of taped autobiography, 43.
105. "Moves to Hilo," *Hawaii Tribune-Herald* (Hilo, TH), October 4, 1942.
106. *Hawaii Tribune-Herald* (Hilo, TH). "Card of Thanks." Advertisement. September 18, 1944, 3.
107. Scheiber and Scheiber, *Bayonets in Paradise*, 213.
108. "Landlord Petition 46377-L," November 6, 1946, Hawayo Takata

Papers. ARC Mss 86, Special Research Collections, UCSB Library, University of California, Santa Barbara, CA.
109. "Landlord Petition 46377-L" (1946).
110. *Honolulu Star-Bulletin* (Honolulu, TH). "Owner's Notice of Completion of Contract." December 11, 1946.
111. Coinnews Media Group, LLC, "Inflation Calculator," US Inflation Calculator.
112. Hailey, Foster. "Hawaii Smiles Again." *New York Times* (New York, NY), October 13, 1946.
113. Marley, Roni. "The Valley House Estate On Kauai Recently Featured at The 2013 Luxury Portfolio Summit." *Hawaii Life* (blog). Entry posted March 6, 2013. https://www.hawaiilife.com/blog/2013-luxury-portfolio-summit/.
114. Marley, Roni. "Kauai's First Hotel and Taylor Camp's Sibling Community – A Narrative Of The Valley House Estate (Part 3)." *Hawaii Life* (blog). Entry posted August 29, 2012. https://www.hawaiilife.com/blog/valley-house-estate-part3/.
115. *Honolulu Star-Bulletin* (Honolulu, TH). "Mainly About People." March 28, 1949.
116. Ray, Dr. Barbara. Interview by the author. St. Petersburg, FL. April 28, 2015.
117. Takata, Transcript of taped autobiography, 71.
118. *Honolulu Star-Bulletin* (Honolulu, TH). "Change of Co-partnership Name." February 10, 1947.
119. Takata, Typewritten autobiography (ca. 1973).
120. *Honolulu Star-Bulletin* (Honolulu, TH). "Notice of Dissolution of Co-partnership." December 22, 1947.
121. *The Honolulu Advertiser* (Honolulu, TH). "Travel Agents Cited to Boost Island Tours." September 14, 1947.
122. *Honolulu Star-Bulletin* (Honolulu, TH). "Waimea Ranch Hotel is Incorporated." October 25, 1947.
123. MacMillan, Richard F. "Aloha Week in Hawaii." *New York Times* (New York, NY), October 10, 1948.
124. Hawayo Takata, "The Art of Healing," ca. 1948, Hawayo Takata Papers. ARC Mss 86, Special Research Collections, UCSB Library, University of California, Santa Barbara, CA.
125. *The Honolulu Advertiser* (Honolulu, TH). "Honolulu Lions Club." October 14, 1957.
126. Straub, Mary. "Reiki: Japanese Method of Healing Could Spark Public Interest Similar to Chinese Acupuncture." *The Star* (Tinley Park, IL), November 13, 1974.
127. Stephanie Mansfield, *The Richest Girl in the World, The Extravagant Life and Fast Times of Doris Duke* (New York, NY: G.P. Putnam's Sons,

1992), 133.

128. Duke, Pony, and Jason Thomas. *Too Rich: The Family Secrets of Doris Duke*. New York, NY: HarperCollins, 1996, 120.

129. Doris Duke Charitable Foundation, Shangri La Museum of Islamic Art, Culture & Design, accessed August 15, 2019, https://www.shangrilahawaii.org/.

130. Mansfield, *The Richest*, 139.

131. Doris Duke to Hawayo Takata, April 23, 1952, Hawayo Takata papers. ARC Mss 86, Special Research Collections, UCSB Library, University of California, Santa Barbara, CA.

132. Ancestry.com, Passenger lists.

133. (Signature illegible) to Hawayo Takata, August 9, 1961, Hawayo Takata papers. ARC Mss 86, Special Research Collections, UCSB Library, University of California, Santa Barbara, CA.

134. "Hawayo Takata: Cash Receipts & Disbursements Statements" (1962).

135. "Hawayo Takata: State of Hawaii Monthly Return," 1960, Hawayo Takata Papers. ARC Mss 86, Special Research Collections, UCSB Library, University of California, Santa Barbara, CA.

136. "Golf Pickups," *The Honolulu Advertiser* (Honolulu, HI), March 31, 1967, 35.

137. Hammond, *We Are All Healers*, 261.

138. Hammond, *We Are All Healers*, 264.

139. *Ka Leo O Na Wahine (The voice of the women)*, American Business Women's Association Honolulu Chapter, I:1, January 1974, collected in Hawayo Takata papers. ARC Mss 86. Special Research Collections, UCSB Library, University of California, Santa Barbara, CA.

140. Patsy Matsuura, "Mrs. Takata and Reiki Power," *Honolulu Advertiser* (Honolulu, HI), February 25, 1974.

141. "Mrs. Takata to Open Office" (1939).

142. Straub, "Reiki: Japanese Method" (1974).

143. *Don Robb Show*, Channel 4 (ABC), April 10, 1974, 1, transcript collected in Hawayo Takata papers. ARC Mss 86. Special Research Collections, UCSB Library, University of California, Santa Barbara, CA.

144. Quodid, The Ultimate Quotation Repository. Accessed August 10, 2019. http://quodid.com/quotes/8552/benjamin-franklin/three-may-keep-a-secret-if-two-of.

145. Jay Jones, "KFC recipe revealed? Tribune shown family scrapbook with 11 herbs and spices," *Chicago Tribune* (Chicago, IL), August 19, 2016, https://www.chicagotribune.com/travel/ct-kfc-recipe-revealed-20160818-story.html.

146. Takata, Transcript of taped autobiography, 17.
147. Yesnie Carrington, telephone interview by the author, St. Petersburg, FL, September 16, 2015.
148. Ray, interview by the author, (2015); Carell Ann Farmer, "The Origin and Validity of the Grandmaster Title and Other Important Issues," Reiki Articles, last modified December 31, 1997, https://www.reiki.org/reikinews/grmaster.html.
149. Ray, *The New Expanded Reference Manual*, 13.
150. Hawayo Takata, Retirement letter, December 1976, Hawayo Takata Papers. ARC Mss 86, Special Research Collections, UCSB Library, University of California, Santa Barbara, CA.
151. Ray, interview by the author (2015).
152. W. G. Morse, Bishop Trust Co. correspondence re setting up trust, 1978, Hawayo Takata Papers. ARC Mss 86, Special Research Collections, UCSB Library, University of California, Santa Barbara, CA.
153. Barbara Jean Weber, "A Comparative Study of the Dido Theme in Virgil, Ovid and Chaucer" (PhD diss., Florida State University, 1970).
154. Barbara D. Weber, "Resume," Hawayo Takata Papers. ARC Mss 86, Special Research Collections, UCSB Library, University of California, Santa Barbara, CA.
155. *Don Robb*, 1.
156. *Don Robb*, 2.
157. Ray and Carrington, *The Official Reiki Handbook* (1982), 4.
158. Author's personal experience.
159. Ray, *The New Expanded Reference Manual*, 13.
160. Ray, *The New Expanded Reference Manual*, 13.
161. Hammond, *We Are All Healers*, ix.
162. Hammond, *We Are All Healers*, x.
163. "Mrs. Takata and Reiki Power" (1974).
164. Kit Kenihan to Hawayo Takata, March 3, 1976, Hawayo Takata papers. ARC Mss 86, Special Research Collections, UCSB Library, University of California, Santa Barbara, CA.
165. Mary Kirkpatrick to Hawayo Takata, June 1, 1975, Hawayo Takata papers. ARC Mss 86, Special Research Collections, UCSB Library, University of California, Santa Barbara, CA.
166. Takata, "The Art of Healing" (ca. 1948).
167. Letters, Hawayo Takata Papers. ARC Mss 86, Special Research Collections, UCSB Library, University of California, Santa Barbara, CA.
168. Carrington, telephone interview by the author (2015); Barbara St. John, interview by the author, Telephone, August 11, 2019.

169. Roy Nickerson, "She is Gentle Healer," *Maui News* (Wailuku, Maui, HI), 1975, collected in Hawayo Takata Papers. ARC Mss 86, Special Research Collections, UCSB Library, University of California, Santa Barbara, CA.

170. Barbara Weber [Ray] to Hawayo Takata, September 4, 1979, Hawayo Takata papers. ARC Mss 86, Special Research Collections, UCSB Library, University of California, Santa Barbara, CA.

171. Hawayo Takata to Dr. Barbara Weber [Ray], September 27, 1979, Private collection of Dr. Barbara Ray, St. Petersburg, FL.

172. Hawayo Takata, Handwritten letter without salutation, May 10, 1979, Hawayo Takata Papers. ARC Mss 86, Special Research Collections, UCSB Library, University of California, Santa Barbara, CA.

173. Takata, Handwritten letter without salutation.

174. Nonie Greene to Hawayo Takata, January 21, 1980, Hawayo Takata papers. ARC Mss 86, Special Research Collections, UCSB Library, University of California, Santa Barbara, CA.

175. Hawayo Takata to Phyllis Furumoto, February 1, 1980, Hawayo Takata papers. ARC Mss 86, Special Research Collections, UCSB Library, University of California, Santa Barbara, CA.

176. Takata to Phyllis Furumoto, June 11, 1980, Hawayo Takata papers. ARC Mss 86, Special Research Collections, UCSB Library, University of California, Santa Barbara, CA.

177. Dr. Barbara Ray, interview by the author, St. Petersburg, FL, June 14, 2019.

178. Ray, interview by the author (2019).

179. Ray, interview by the author (2019).

180. Takata to Furumoto, February 1, 1980.

181. Takata to Furumoto, June 11, 1980.

182. Ray, interview by the author (2015).

183. Dr. Barbara Weber Ray et al. to Reiki Masters, March 7, 1983, TRTIA Archives, The Radiance Technique International Association, Inc., St. Petersburg, FL.

184. Ray et al. to Reiki Masters (1983).

185. Ray, interview by the author (2015).

186. Hawayo Takata to Miss Bowling, August 8, 1980, Hawayo Takata papers. ARC Mss 86, Special Research Collections, UCSB Library, University of California, Santa Barbara, CA.

187. Dr. Barbara Weber [Ray] to Hawayo Takata, August 27, 1980, Hawayo Takata papers. ARC Mss 86, Special Research Collections, UCSB Library, University of California, Santa Barbara, CA.

188. "In Memorial - Master Hawayo Takata," *The Reiki Review* I, no. 1 (Spring 1981): 1.

189. Letter by Dr. Barbara Weber [Ray], February 8, 1981, TRTIA Archives, The Radiance Technique International Association, Inc., St. Petersburg, FL.
190. Erin Meyer, *The Culture Map: Breaking Through the Invisible Boundaries of Global Business* (New York, NY: PublicAffairs, 2014), 39.
191. Meyer, *The Culture Map*, 42.
192. Ray, *The New Expanded Reference Manual*, 14.
193. Martha Taub to Hawayo Takata, July 23, 1980, Hawayo Takata papers. ARC Mss 86, Special Research Collections, UCSB Library, University of California, Santa Barbara, CA.
194. Taub to Takata.
195. Meyer, *The Culture Map*, 130.
196. Meyer, *The Culture Map*, 125.
197. St. John, telephone interview by the author (2019).
198. Alice Furumoto, "Alice Takata's Notes for Grey Book," 1981, Hawayo Takata Papers. ARC Mss 86, Special Research Collections, UCSB Library, University of California, Santa Barbara, CA.
199. David Bohm, *Wholeness and the Implicate Order* (London, England: Ark Paperbacks, 1980), 16.
200. Farmer, "The Origin," Reiki Articles.
201. Carrington, telephone interview by the author (2015).
202. Phyllis Furumoto to Barbara Weber Ray, May 14, 1983, Hawayo Takata papers. ARC Mss 86, Special Research Collections, UCSB Library, University of California, Santa Barbara, CA.
203. Phyllis Furumoto to Barbara Weber Ray, May 19, 1983, Private collection of Dr. Barbara Ray, St. Petersburg, FL.
204. Furumoto to Ray, May 19, 1983.
205. Barbara L. McCullough to Phyllis Furumoto, November 28, 1982, Hawayo Takata papers. ARC Mss 86, Special Research Collections, UCSB Library, University of California, Santa Barbara, CA.
206. Farmer, "The Origin," Reiki Articles.
207. Carrington, telephone interview by the author (2015).
208. Ray, *The New Expanded Reference Manual*, 11.
209. Ray, *The New Expanded Reference Manual*, 223.
210. *Morning Edition*, "Wikipedia Policies Limit Editing Haymarket Bombing," National Public Radio, first broadcast October 3, 2012, hosted by Steve Inskeep, accessed April 27, 2019, https://www.npr.org/2012/10/03/162203092/wikipedia-politicizes-landmark-historical-event.
211. David J. Linden, *Touch: The Science of Hand, Heart and Mind* (New York, NY: Viking, 2015), 11.
212. Linden, *Touch: The Science*, 11.
213. Tiffany Field, "American adolescents touch each other less and are

more aggressive toward their peers as compared with French adolescents," *Adolescence* 34, no. 136 (Winter 1999): 754.

214. Tiffany Field, *Touch*, 2nd ed. (Cambridge, MA: The MIT Press, 2014), 24.

215. Linden, *Touch: The Science*, 5.

216. Field, *Touch*, 40.

217. Field, *Touch*, 189.

218. "Mrs. Takata to Open Office" (1939).

219. Unilever United States, Home page, Q-tips, accessed September 3, 2019, https://www.qtips.com.

220. Ray and Carrington, *The Official Reiki Handbook* (1982), 4.

221. United States Patent and Trademark Office, "Search trademark database," United States Patent and Trademark Office, accessed August 26, 2019, https://www.uspto.gov/trademarks-application-process/search-trademark-database.

222. Anonymous translation of *Hawaii Hochi* articles, 1937, Hawayo Takata Papers. ARC Mss 86, Special Research Collections, UCSB Library, University of California, Santa Barbara, CA.

223. Coinnews Media Group, LLC, "Inflation Calculator," US Inflation Calculator.

224. Ray, interview by the author (2012).

225. Dr. Barbara Ray, *The Official Handbook of The Radiance Technique*®, *Authentic Reiki*®, fourth ed. (St. Petersburg, FL: The Radiance Technique International Association & Radiance Seminars, 2019), 34-36.

226. The Radiance Technique International Association, "Certification and Qualifications," TRTIA, accessed July 19, 2019, https://www.trtia.org/decert.htm.

227. *First American-International Reiki Association Conference* (Atlanta, GA: A.I.R.A., 1983).

228. "Psychic Reading." Recording. California, ca. 1974. Hawayo Takata papers. ARC Mss 86. Special Research Collections, UCSB Library, University of California, Santa Barbara, CA.

229. "Second and Third Degree Networking Projects," *The Reiki Review* IV, no. 1 (December 1983): 4.

230. "High Noon Reiki Network for World Peace," *The Reiki Journal* V, no. 2 (July-September 1985): 4.

231. "The Radiant TRT Heart First Ashram®," *The Radiance Technique Journal* 3, no. 1 (Autumn 1998): 13.

232. See Appendix C.

BIBLIOGRAPHY

The databases accessed through Ancestry.com are not referenced individually within this source listing. They include but are not limited to birth and death records, censuses, passenger lists, telephone directories (which in the early twentieth century included professions), school yearbooks, and more.

Note: publications from the Hawaiian Islands before statehood are cited with the two-letter abbreviation TH — Territory of Hawaii — as was customary. When the U.S. Post Office introduced two-letter state abbreviations in October 1963, Hawaii became "HI."

Ancestry.com. "Passenger Lists, at al." Ancestry.com Operations, Inc. https://www.ancestry.com.

Anonymous translation of *Hawaii Hochi* articles. 1937. Hawayo Takata Papers. ARC Mss 86. Special Research Collections, UCSB Library, University of California, Santa Barbara, CA.

Bohm, David. *Wholeness and the Implicate Order.* London, England: Ark Paperbacks, 1980.

Carrington, Yesnie. Telephone interview by the author. St. Petersburg, FL. September 16, 2015.

Coinnews Media Group, LLC. "Inflation Calculator." US Inflation Calculator. Accessed August 11, 2019. https://www.usinflationcalculator.com.

Daws, Gavin. *Shoal of Time, A History of the Hawaiian Islands.* New York, NY: The MacMillan Company, 1968.

Don Robb Show [transcript]. Channel 4 (ABC). April 10, 1974.

Doris Duke Charitable Foundation. Shangri La Museum of Islamic Art, Culture & Design. Accessed August 15, 2019. https://www.shangrilahawaii.org/.

Dr. Chujiro Hayashi. 1937-38. Photograph. TRTIA Archives. The Radiance Technique International Association, Inc., St. Petersburg, FL.

Dr. Mikao Usui. Undated. Photograph. TRTIA Archives. The Radiance Technique International Association, Inc., St. Petersburg, FL.

Duke, Doris. Letter to Hawayo Takata, April 23, 1952. Hawayo Takata papers. ARC Mss 86. Special Research Collections, UCSB Library, University of California, Santa Barbara, CA.

Duke, Pony, and Jason Thomas. *Too Rich: The Family Secrets of Doris Duke.* New York, NY: HarperCollins, 1996.

Farmer, Carell Ann. "The Origin and Validity of the Grandmaster Title and Other Important Issues." Reiki Articles. Last modified December 31, 1997.https://www.reiki.org/reikinews/grmaster.html.

Field, Tiffany. "American adolescents touch each other less and are more aggressive toward their peers as compared with French adolescents." *Adolescence* 34, no. 136 (Winter 1999): 753-58.

———. *Touch.* 2nd ed. Cambridge, MA: The MIT Press, 2014.

———. "Touch for socioemotional and physical well-being: A review." *Developmental Review* 30 (2010): 367-83. https://doi.org/10.1016/j.dr.2011.01.001.

———. "Violence and Touch Deprivation in Adolescents." *Adolescence* 37, no. 148 (Winter 2002): 735-49.

First American-International Reiki Association Conference. Atlanta, GA: A.I.R.A., 1983.

Furumoto, Alice. "Alice Takata's Notes for Grey Book." 1981. Hawayo Takata Papers. ARC Mss 86. Special Research Collections, UCSB Library, University of California, Santa Barbara, CA.

Furumoto, Phyllis. Letter to Barbara Weber Ray, May 19, 1983. Private collection of Dr. Barbara Ray, St. Petersburg, FL.

———. Letter to Barbara Weber Ray, May 14, 1983. Hawayo Takata papers. ARC Mss 86. Special Research Collections, UCSB Library, University of California, Santa Barbara, CA.

The Garden Island (Lihue, TH). "Japanese Buy Thrift Stamps." March 12, 1918.

The Garden Island (Lihue, TH). "Legion Dance is Huge Success." April 25, 1922.

The Garden Island (Lihue, TH). "Makee Sugar Co." December 22, 1914.

The Garden Island (Lihue, TH). "Owns Land in Every Quarter of Globe." November 19, 1912.

The Garden Island (Lihue, TH). "Reiki Sanitarium Treatments. " Advertisement. October 13, 1936.

The Garden Island (Lihue, TH). "Wailua Golf Club Holds First Tournament." November 8, 1921.

Graham, Vera. "Mrs. Takata Opens Minds to Reiki." *The Times* (San Mateo, CA), May 17, 1975.

Greene, Nonie. Letter to Hawayo Takata, January 21, 1980. Hawayo Takata papers. ARC Mss 86. Special Research Collections, UCSB Library, University of California, Santa Barbara, CA.

Hailey, Foster. "Hawaii Smiles Again." *New York Times* (New York, NY), October 13, 1946.

Hammond, Sally. *We Are All Healers.* New York, NY: Harper & Row, 1973.

Hawaiian Gazette (Honolulu, TH). "Married an Italian Nobleman." September 18, 1903.

Hawaii Tribune-Herald (Hilo, TH). "At Hilo Hotel." May 24, 1939.

Hawaii Tribune-Herald (Hilo, TH). "Card of Thanks." Advertisement. September 18, 1944.

Hawaii Tribune-Herald (Hilo, TH). "Group Enjoys Mahjongg Party." April

6, 1941.

Hawaii Tribune-Herald (Hilo, TH). "Health Studio." Advertisement. December 7, 1940.

Hawaii Tribune-Herald (Hilo, TH). "Honors Mother." May 26, 1941.

Hawaii Tribune-Herald (Hilo, TH). "Misses Hirata, Martin Assist Mrs. Takata." August 27, 1939.

Hawaii Tribune-Herald (Hilo, TH). "Moves to Hilo." October 4, 1942.

Hawaii Tribune-Herald (Hilo, TH). "Mrs. Takata and Daughters to Honolulu." August 30, 1939.

Hawaii Tribune-Herald (Hilo, TH). "Mrs. Takata to Open Office." May 28, 1939.

Hawaii Tribune-Herald (Hilo, TH). "Reiki Treatments." November 13, 1939.

"Hawayo Takata: Cash Receipts & Disbursements Statements." 1962. Hawayo Takata Papers. ARC Mss 86. Special Research Collections, UCSB Library, University of California, Santa Barbara, CA.

Hawayo Takata & Dr. Barbara Ray. August 1980. Photograph. TRTIA Archives. The Radiance Technique International Association, Inc., St. Petersburg, FL.

Hawayo Takata in long dress. ca. 1978. Photograph. TRTIA Archives. The Radiance Technique International Association, Inc., St. Petersburg, FL.

"Hawayo Takata: State of Hawaii Monthly Return." 1960. Hawayo Takata Papers. ARC Mss 86. Special Research Collections, UCSB Library, University of California, Santa Barbara, CA.

Hawayo Takata wearing A.R.A. T-shirt. 1980. Photograph. TRTIA Archives. The Radiance Technique International Association, Inc., St. Petersburg, FL.

Hayashi, Chujiro. Memorandum to Hawayo Takata, memorandum, February 21, 1938. Private collection of Dr. Barbara Ray, St. Petersburg, FL.

———. Memorandum to Hawayo Takata, memorandum, "(First Degree)," December 13, 1935. Hawayo Takata papers. ARC Mss 86. Special Research Collections, UCSB Library, University of California, Santa Barbara, CA.

———. Memorandum to Hawayo Takata, memorandum, "(Third Degree)," October 1, 1936. Hawayo Takata papers. ARC Mss 86. Special Research Collections, UCSB Library, University of California, Santa Barbara, CA.

"High Noon Reiki Network for World Peace." *The Reiki Journal* V, no. 2 (July-September 1985).

Hilo Hongwanji Mission. Memorandum to Hawayo Takata, memorandum, "Resolution of Appreciation," December 11, 1961. Hawayo Takata papers. ARC Mss 86. Special Research Collections,

UCSB Library, University of California, Santa Barbara, CA.
Home. Maeda Hospital. https://www.maeda-hospital-tokyo.jp/.
The Honolulu Advertiser (Honolulu, HI). "Golf Pickups." March 31, 1967.
The Honolulu Advertiser (Honolulu, TH). "Honolulu Lions Club." October 14, 1957.
The Honolulu Advertiser (Honolulu, TH). "Travel Agents Cited to Boost Island Tours." September 14, 1947.
Honolulu Star-Bulletin (Honolulu, TH). "Change of Co-partnership Name." February 10, 1947.
Honolulu Star-Bulletin (Honolulu, TH). "Col. Spalding is Paid Honor." April 24, 1930.
Honolulu Star-Bulletin (Honolulu, TH). "Land Court Deeds." October 24, 1939.
Honolulu Star-Bulletin (Honolulu, TH). "Mainly About People." March 28, 1949.
Honolulu Star-Bulletin (Honolulu, TH). "Notice of Dissolution of Co-partnership." December 22, 1947.
Honolulu Star-Bulletin (Honolulu, TH). "Owner's Notice of Completion of Contract." December 11, 1946.
Honolulu Star-Bulletin (Honolulu, TH). "Some Favorite Local Recipes." July 22, 1926.
Honolulu Star-Bulletin (Honolulu, TH). "13 Leaving for S.F. for Y.M.B.A. Meet." July 8, 1932.
Honolulu Star-Bulletin (Honolulu, TH). "Three Kauai Officials In." January 7, 1931.
Honolulu Star-Bulletin (Honolulu, TH). "Waimea Ranch Hotel is Incorporated." October 25, 1947.
Honolulu Star-Bulletin (Honolulu, TH). "Y.M.B.A. Party Sails Thursday." July 13, 1932.
Honpa Hongwanji Hawaii Betsuin. "Temple History." Honpa Hongwanji Hawaii Betsuin. Accessed August 9, 2019. https://hawaiibetsuin.org/temple-history/.
"In Memorial - Master Hawayo Takata." *The Reiki Review* I, no. 1 (Spring 1981): 1.
Jones, Jay. "KFC recipe revealed? Tribune shown family scrapbook with 11 herbs and spices." *Chicago Tribune* (Chicago, IL), August 19, 2016. https://www.chicagotribune.com/travel/ct-kfc-recipe-revealed-20160818-story.html.
Ka Leo O Na Wahine (The voice of the women), January 1974.
Kenihan, Kit. Letter to Hawayo Takata, March 3, 1976. Hawayo Takata papers. ARC Mss 86. Special Research Collections, UCSB Library, University of California, Santa Barbara, CA.
Kirkpatrick, Mary. Letter to Hawayo Takata, June 1, 1975. Hawayo Takata papers. ARC Mss 86. Special Research Collections, UCSB

Bibliography

Library, University of California, Santa Barbara, CA.

"Landlord Petition 46377-L." November 6, 1946. Hawayo Takata Papers. ARC Mss 86. Special Research Collections, UCSB Library, University of California, Santa Barbara, CA.

Linden, David J. *Touch: The Science of Hand, Heart and Mind.* New York, NY: Viking, 2015.

MacMillan, Richard F. "Aloha Week in Hawaii." *New York Times* (New York, NY), October 10, 1948.

Mansfield, Stephanie. *The Richest Girl in the World, The Extravagant Life and Fast Times of Doris Duke.* New York, NY: G.P. Putnam's Sons, 1992.

Mantis, Irene, Marisa Mercuri, Dale M. Stack, and Tiffany M. Field. "Depressed and non-depressed mothers' touching during social interactions with their infants." *Developmental Cognitive Neuroscience* 35 (February 2019): 57-65. https://doi.org/10.1016/j.dcn.2018.01.005.

Marley, Roni. "Kauai's First Hotel and Taylor Camp's Sibling Community - A Narrative Of The Valley House Estate (Part 3)." *Hawaii Life* (blog). Entry posted August 29, 2012. https://www.hawaiilife.com/blog/valley-house-estate-part3/.

———. "The Valley House Estate On Kauai Recently Featured at The 2013 Luxury Portfolio Summit." *Hawaii Life* (blog). Entry posted March 6, 2013. https://www.hawaiilife.com/blog/2013-luxury-portfolio-summit/.

Matsuura, Patsy. "Mrs. Takata and Reiki Power." *Honolulu Advertiser* (Honolulu, HI), February 25, 1974.

McCullough, Barbara L. Letter to Phyllis Furumoto, November 28, 1982. Hawayo Takata papers. ARC Mss 86. Special Research Collections, UCSB Library, University of California, Santa Barbara, CA.

Meyer, Erin. *The Culture Map: Breaking Through the Invisible Boundaries of Global Business.* New York, NY: PublicAffairs, 2014.

Morning Edition. "Wikipedia Policies Limit Editing Haymarket Bombing." National Public Radio. First broadcast October 3, 2012. Hosted by Steve Inskeep. Accessed April 27, 2019. https://www.npr.org/2012/10/03/162203092/wikipedia-politicizes-landmark-historical-event.

Morse, W. G. Bishop Trust Co. correspondence re setting up trust. 1978. Hawayo Takata Papers. ARC Mss 86. Special Research Collections, UCSB Library, University of California, Santa Barbara, CA.

Nakamura, Kelli Y. "Wilfred Tsukiyama." Densho Encyclopedia. Accessed August 10, 2019. http://encyclopedia.densho.org/Wilfred%20Tsukiyama/.

Nellist, George F. "Statewide County HI Archives Biographies.....Makee, James November 24, 1812 - September 16, 1879." In *USGenWeb Archives*. Previously published as "The Story of Hawaii and Its

Builders." *The Honolulu Star Bulletin* (Territory of Hawaii), 1925. Accessed July 22, 2019. http://files.usgwarchives.net/hi/statewide/bios/makee49bs.txt.

Nickerson, Roy. "She is Gentle Healer." *Maui News* (Wailuku, Maui, HI), 1975.

Nordyke, Eleanor C., and Y. Scott Matsumoto. "Japanese in Hawaii: a Historical and Demographic Perspective." In *eVols*. Honolulu, HI: Hawaiian Historical Society, n.d. Previously published in *Hawaiian Journal of History* 11 (1977). Accessed May 23, 2019. http://hdl.handle.net/10524/528.

Ogawa, Dennis M., and Glen Grant. *Kodomo No Tame Ni-For the Sake of the Children: The Japanese-American Experience in Hawaii*. Honolulu, HI: University of Hawaii Press, 1980. Google.

Okahata, James H., ed. *A History of Japanese in Hawaii*. Honolulu, HI: The United Japanese Society of Hawaii, 1971.

"Pagh." Memory Alpha. Accessed June 15, 2019. https://memory-alpha.fandom.com/wiki/Pagh.

"Psychic Reading." Recording. California ca. 1974. Hawayo Takata papers. ARC Mss 86. Special Research Collections, UCSB Library, University of California, Santa Barbara, CA.

Quodid, The Ultimate Quotation Repository. Accessed August 10, 2019. http://Quodid.com.

The Radiance Technique International Association. "Certification and Qualifications." TRTIA. Accessed July 19, 2019. https://www.trtia.org/decert.htm.

———. "Purposes of The Radiance Technique International Association, Inc." TRTIA. Accessed June 18, 2019. https://www.trtia.org/purposes.htm.

"The Radiant TRT Heart First Ashram®." *The Radiance Technique Journal* 3, no. 1 (Autumn 1998).

Ray, Barbara, Ph.D. *The Reiki Factor*. Smithtown, NY: Exposition Press, Inc., 1983.

———. *The 'Reiki' Factor in The Radiance Technique®*. Expanded ed. St. Petersburg, FL: Radiance Associates, 1992.

Ray, Barbara Weber, Ph.D., and Yesnie Carrington. *The Official Reiki Handbook*. St. Petersburg, FL: American- International Reiki Association, 1982.

Ray, Dr. Barbara. "Energy Model." Graphic. 1984.

———. Interview by the author. St. Petersburg, FL. April 28, 2015.

———. Interview by the author. St. Petersburg, FL. August 4, 2012.

———. Interview by the author. St. Petersburg, FL. June 14, 2019.

———. *The New Expanded Reference Manual of The Radiance Technique®, Authentic Reiki®*. Third ed. St. Petersburg, FL: Radiance Associates, 2013.

————. *The Official Handbook of The Radiance Technique*®, *Authentic Reiki*®. Fourth ed. St. Petersburg, FL: The Radiance Technique International Association & Radiance Seminars, 2019.

Ray, Dr. Barbara Weber, Nonie C. Greene, Virginia W. Samdahl, and Barbara St. John. Letter to Reiki Masters, March 7, 1983. TRTIA Archives. The Radiance Technique International Association, Inc., St. Petersburg, FL.

"Reception Honors Japanese Visitor." ca. 1937. Hawayo Takata Papers. ARC Mss 86. Special Research Collections, UCSB Library, University of California, Santa Barbara, CA.

Reception in honor of Master Hawayo Takata. August 1980. Illustration. TRTIA Archives. The Radiance Technique International Association, Inc., St. Petersburg, FL.

"Reiki Slaw." *The Reiki Review* I, no. 1 (Spring 1981): 2.

Russ, William A., Jr. "The Role of Sugar in Hawaiian Annexation." *The Pacific Historical Review* XII, no. 4 (December 1943): 339-50.

Sanitarium. "Moments that made us: Our Story." Sanitarium. Accessed August 14, 2019. https://www.sanitarium.co.nz/about/sanitarium-story/history.

The San Juan Star (San Juan, PR). "Mrs. Takata opens door to Japanese healing art." July 20, 1979.

Scheiber, Harry N., and Jane L. Scheiber. *Bayonets in Paradise: Martial Law in Hawai'i during World War II*. University of Hawai'i Press, 2016. Kindle edition.

"Second and Third Degree Networking Projects." *The Reiki Review* IV, no. 1 (December 1983).

(Signature illegible). Letter to Hawayo Takata, August 9, 1961. Hawayo Takata papers. ARC Mss 86. Special Research Collections, UCSB Library, University of California, Santa Barbara, CA.

Smithsonian Institution. "Hawaii - History and Heritage." Smithsonian.com. Last modified November 6, 2007. https://www.smithsonianmag.com/travel/hawaii-history-and-heritage-4164590/.

Soboleski, Hank. "Kauai's Spalding Monument." *The Garden Island* (Lihue, HI), April 29, 2018.

Special to The New York Times. "COL. Z. M. SPALDING, EX-NEW YORKER, DEAD." *New York Times (1923-Current file)*; Jun 21, 1927; ProQuest Historical Newspapers: The New York Times, 25.

"State Abbreviations." United States Postal Service. https://about.usps.com/who-we-are/postal-history/state-abbreviations.htm.

St. John, Barbara. Interview by the author. Telephone. August 11, 2019.

Straub, Mary. "Reiki: Japanese Method of Healing Could Spark Public Interest Similar to Chinese Acupuncture." *The Star* (Tinley Park, IL),

November 13, 1974.

Sullivan, Maxine H. Letter to Nonie C. Greene, July 6, 1983. TRTIA Archives. The Radiance Technique International Association, Inc., St. Petersburg, FL.

Takata, Hawayo. "The Art of Healing." ca. 1948. Hawayo Takata Papers. ARC Mss 86. Special Research Collections, UCSB Library, University of California, Santa Barbara, CA.

————. Handwritten autobiography. ca. 1973. Hawayo Takata Papers. ARC Mss 86. Special Research Collections, UCSB Library, University of California, Santa Barbara, CA.

————. Handwritten letter without salutation. May 10, 1979. Hawayo Takata Papers. ARC Mss 86. Special Research Collections, UCSB Library, University of California, Santa Barbara, CA.

————. Letter to Dr. Barbara Weber, September 27, 1979. Private collection of Dr. Barbara Ray, St. Petersburg, FL.

————. Letter to Miss Bowling, August 8, 1980. Hawayo Takata papers. ARC Mss 86. Special Research Collections, UCSB Library, University of California, Santa Barbara, CA.

————. Letter to Phyllis Furumoto, June 11, 1980. Hawayo Takata papers. ARC Mss 86. Special Research Collections, UCSB Library, University of California, Santa Barbara, CA.

————. Letter to Phyllis Furumoto, February 1, 1980. Hawayo Takata papers. ARC Mss 86. Special Research Collections, UCSB Library, University of California, Santa Barbara, CA.

————. "Reiki Sanitarium Treatments." Advertisement. *The Garden Island* (Kauai, TH), October 13, 1936.

————. Retirement letter. December 1976. Hawayo Takata Papers. ARC Mss 86. Special Research Collections, UCSB Library, University of California, Santa Barbara, CA.

————. Transcript of Dr. Usui story. August 24, 1980. The Radiance Technique International Association, Inc., St. Petersburg, FL.

————. Transcript of taped autobiography. December 1979. The Radiance Technique International Association, Inc., St. Petersburg, FL.

————. Typewritten autobiography. ca. 1973. Hawayo Takata Papers. ARC Mss 86. Special Research Collections, UCSB Library, University of California, Santa Barbara, CA.

Taub, Martha. Letter to Hawayo Takata, July 23, 1980. Hawayo Takata papers. ARC Mss 86. Special Research Collections, UCSB Library, University of California, Santa Barbara, CA.

"Temple History." Honpa Hongwanji Hawaii Betsuin. Accessed August 7, 2019. https://hawaiibetsuin.org/temple-history/.

Thomas, Henry W., and Gertrude Thomas. *Harvesting Sugar Cane*. 1912. Photograph. Accessed August 9, 2019. http://www.huapala.net/document/42.

Bibliography

Hawaiian Historical Society Historical Photograph Collection
Tummons, Patricia. "Early Developers of Leilani Estates Ignored the Eruption in Their Back Yard." *Environment Hawai'i*, June 2018. https://www.environment-hawaii.org/?p=10407.

Unilever United States. Home page. Q-tips. Accessed September 3, 2019. https://www.qtips.com.
First accessed in September 2015; notice continues to be at the bottom of the home page four years later.

United States Patent and Trademark Office. "Search trademark database." United States Patent and Trademark Office. Accessed August 26, 2019. https://www.uspto.gov/trademarks-application-process/search-trademark-database.

U.S. Department of the Interior. "Pacific Island Network Vital Signs Monitoring Plan." National Park Service. Last modified September 29, 2004. https://irma.nps.gov/DataStore/DownloadFile/575333.

Wakukawa, Ernest K. *A History of the Japanese People in Hawaii*. Honolulu, TH: The Tokyo Shoin, 1938.

Weber [Ray], Barbara D. Resume. Hawayo Takata Papers. ARC Mss 86. Special Research Collections, UCSB Library, University of California, Santa Barbara, CA.

Weber [Ray], Barbara Jean. "A Comparative Study of the Dido Theme in Virgil, Ovid and Chaucer." PhD diss., Florida State University, 1970.

Weber [Ray], Dr. Barbara. Letter, February 8, 1981. TRTIA Archives. The Radiance Technique International Association, Inc., St. Petersburg, FL.

———. Letter to Hawayo Takata, September 4, 1979. Hawayo Takata papers. ARC Mss 86. Special Research Collections, UCSB Library, University of California, Santa Barbara, CA.

———. Letter to Hawayo Takata, August 27, 1980. Hawayo Takata papers. ARC Mss 86. Special Research Collections, UCSB Library, University of California, Santa Barbara, CA.

A Wikimedia Project. "Talk:Socrates." Wikiquote. Last modified July 29, 2017. https://en.wikiquote.org/wiki/Talk:Socrates.

Williams, James J. *Lihue Village, 1887*. Photograph. Accessed August 9, 2019. http://www.huapala.net/document/6809.

Hawaiian Historical Society Historical Photograph Collection
Woodruff, Lisa. "Why the Magic Art of Tidying Up Doesn't Work for American Women." Review of *The Life-changing Magic of Tidying Up*. Organize 365. Accessed August 21, 2019. https://organize365.com/magic-art-tidying-review/.

Young, Peter T. "Colonel Zephaniah Swift Spalding." Images of Old Hawai'i. Last modified February 3, 2015. http://imagesofoldhawaii.com/colonel-zephaniah-swift-spalding/.

Printed in Great Britain
by Amazon

54934085R00104